# Waves of Pink

## STORIES OF SISTERHOOD

CURATED BY
JULIE PERSHING

**Waves of Pink: Stories of Sisterhood**



Delo Fercho
Andrea Davis
Tami Starkey
April Everist
Annie Hunnicutt
Danielle Cooper
Deb Hart
Leslie Kerwin Myll
Robin Ray-Rutherford
Becci Owens
Kortnee Colbry
Shannon Preston

Cover Design: Michael McCartney - DezignZ by Soup
Proof Editing: Roger Shipman
Interior Formatting and Graphics: Julie Pershing



ISBN: 978-1-947894-12-9

**Printed in USA**

# Dedication

This book is dedicated to the caretakers. Husbands, partners, significant others, and family and friends who support loved ones diagnosed with breast cancer.

The caretakers are there, in the tender moments and the tough times. Learning to be an advocate. Navigating the healthcare system, dispensing medications, and dressing wounds. Caring for a loved one with no formal training. Crying, laughing, staying up through sleepless nights, and giving every piece of themselves.

People will ask how the person they are caring for is feeling, but how often do we ask how the caretaker is doing?

Thank you doesn't feel like it's enough, but our deep gratitude seems like the right place to begin.

Julie Pershing

Help us to create support and encouragement for survivors.

- Share your story and picture on social media! Hold a copy of Waves of Pink using the hashtag:
  #wavesofpink

- Free PDF: Get a FREE full color PDF copy of the quotes featured in Waves of Pink:
  www.gallivantpress/pinkquotes

- Visit our website: www.pinksistas.org

Gallivant Press proudly supports Pink Sistas

# Table of Contents

# Introduction

Sisterhood. What does it mean? It's a bond between women. Sisterhood can be a bond between sisters as siblings, or a bond between women who are linked by something they have in common.

There is a Sisterhood of women who are diagnosed with breast cancer. It is a Sisterhood no one in their right mind would ever want to be a part of, but here they are.

One in eight women is diagnosed with breast cancer. One in eight women joins the Sisterhood. One in eight women who did not ask to join, one in eight who are not offered an option to say "No, I don't want membership in the Sisterhood."

Young and old, all races, all colors. Women with small children, women with grown children. Wives, sisters, mothers, girlfriends, lovers and friends. All part of the Sisterhood no one wants, one they didn't know they would be required to join.

You wonder how they cope. How does a young woman who is not "old enough" for a mammogram have breast cancer? How does a single mom have breast cancer? How does a sister have it? How does a wife have it? A mother, grandmother, a friend? Where does it come from—why them, why us, why me.

The stories you will read in this book are written by those women, the women in the Sisterhood.

They are strong, stronger even than they realize. They are warriors who were forced to navigate "the journey," and who are there to help the next one to navigate hers.

When someone comes along and reaches out a hand and says, "I know what you need, you need to connect with a positive, healing group of women," grab their hand and let them lift you up. Sometimes what we need is to simply bond with friends, a gentle hug and a quiet understanding.

These are the stories of the women I would want in my corner, fighting with me, supporting and encouraging me. Knowing what I was going through. These are the women I want as my friends.

Pink Sistas offers women who have been diagnosed with breast cancer a no-cost weekend retreat where they find rest and relaxation and meet other women who are navigating "the journey."

For more information on how you can support this incredible organization, please visit https://pinksistas.org/

Julie Pershing

Faith Love
HOPE
Victory
Support
Win
Awareness
Strength
Determination
Courage
Fight
Believe

# Roller Coaster

I went into the doctor for a routine mammogram. While I was still at the hospital getting the mammogram, the technician came to me and said she needed to have the doctor read my mammogram. The doctor asked me if I would go over to another hospital and have a biopsy that day.

My husband Randy and I have been together for fifteen years. He was working that day, and he wasn't able to go with me. My dad came from Kelso, Washington, to meet me at the hospital in Portland, Oregon, for the biopsy.

After they take a biopsy, you get to wait three days for the results. Three long days.

My biopsy happened to be on a Thursday, so I didn't get the results until the following Monday. It was a very long and stressful weekend.

## The Call

I clearly remember the moment the nurse navigator called and told me I had ductal carcinoma. I didn't know anything about breast cancer at the time so the only word I heard was carcinoma. What flashed through my brain was "That's cancer."

Ductal carcinoma is a common type of breast cancer that starts in cells that line the milk ducts. In most cases, surgery is the first treatment for invasive ductal carcinoma.

The nurse navigator gave me some basic information and a surgeon's name. Nurse navigators are supposed to serve as the primary contact for the patient through every step of their care, using their skills and knowledge to offer patients special insight on their diagnosis and upcoming treatment journey.

Unfortunately, the call with the nurse navigator was my only contact with her. She did not offer me anything other than the name of the surgeon and never followed up with me after the call. I was left to figure out my treatment journey on my own.

When I hung up from the nurse, I texted my daughter Tiffany, my niece Tara, and my husband Randy. I said, "I need to tell you guys something." The hardest part about telling them was that I was embarrassed to say I had cancer.

They were asking me questions I had no answers for. I felt like I was on a roller coaster that I had no control over.

*What's next?*

I had no clue.

## Removing the Cancer

At my next appointment we scheduled a lumpectomy; it's where the surgeons go in and cut out a large part of your breast to try to remove the cancer cells.

When breast cancer is surgically removed during a surgical biopsy, lumpectomy or mastectomy, a rim of normal tissue surrounding the tumor is also removed. This rim is called a margin. Margins help show whether or not all of the tumor was removed.

The doctor removes cells then checks the margins around where the cells were removed. They keep removing cells until they get clear margins. Once your cells test positive for clear margins, it means no cancer cells are in the area outside of the cancer they cut out.

When I woke up from the surgery, I was really sore. I asked the surgeon, "Why am I so sore if you just did a lumpectomy?" He told me they took about a 3"×4" piece out of my breast and weren't able to get clear margins. This meant more surgery would be needed to remove any remaining cancer cells.

I had to be my own advocate, so I asked, "What do we do next?" It was disappointing to have to figure everything out by myself. The doctor told me they would need to remove the remaining breast tissue. My first thought was, What about the other side? Will I be lopsided? When I asked, he said after recovery they could do reconstruction surgery to make my breasts look the same.

Randy went to every appointment with me. He only missed one appointment, and my stepdaughter Heather went with me to that one.

I talked with the doctors about my options for reconstruction. They were very matter-of-fact and told me I could get implants at the same time as my double mastectomy surgery.

This was the appointment Heather went to with me. They showed us pictures of women with implants. It was very emotional for me; the book had pictures of women's torsos, from the belly to the neck. I thought the pictures looked like cadavers. I was scared and started crying. The pictures showed what it might look like with and without implants. I cried and cried; it was so hard to look at the pictures.

I was told the type of implants they would use were the "safest" implants, smooth like a gummy bear. I was not given the full information needed to make an informed decision. There was nothing said about what could go wrong. No one told me the lifespan of implants is only ten years, and the FDA recommends you get an MRI every year for the first three years, and once every three years after that.

I was not made aware of the disadvantages, and I opted to get immediate reconstruction with implants at the same time as my double mastectomy. I felt I needed the confidence boost after everything I had been going through and wanted to feel and look like myself. I just knew this would be my last surgery.

I didn't want any more surgeries. I think I was channeling my aunt Janet who also had breast cancer. She ended up dying; I don't know if it was breast cancer or what that she eventually died from, but I knew I didn't want to die. I opted to have both breasts removed at the same time.

We made the appointment for my double mastectomy. I had to wait four weeks until I could go in for the surgery. I was amazed when about twenty people came to the hospital to see me off to surgery. I had a conversation with my Aunt Ruth prior to surgery. I knew I needed someone to come and help take care of me afterward, and she was the only person I wanted to take care of me in my recovery. I was relieved when she said she would come and stay after the surgery.

Randy was there with me through the appointments, the surgery, and recovery. But he still had to work, and I didn't know what to expect after a double mastectomy, I just knew that Aunt Ruth would have answers—and she did. She helped care for me and put me on a twenty-four-hour medication timetable so we would know when I should take my medicines.

And let me tell you, the pain is excruciating. You want to keep on top of the pain right after surgery and take your medication right on time, or the pain will get ahold of you. Then you have to basically start over, trying to get back on top of the pain.

About a month later, I developed large holes at the bottom of my breast where my skin was separating. I had to go back in to have one side fixed. The next week, the doctor had to go in and fix the other side.

I slept in the recliner and Randy on the couch the whole time I was recovering. He was always there for me, through the diagnosis, appointments, surgeries, and recovery.

My dog Oliver slept on my lap and seemed to know when I needed rest. He's been so sweet and gently pats my chest when he lies with me as if he knows what I've been through.

"Ah," I thought, "this will be my last surgery. I am going to get into CrossFit and really take care of myself—this is a new lease on life!" I joined a CrossFit gym and was beginning to get into really good shape. I had the opportunity to be on a dragon boat team. I was excited to join; the team is made up of about 110 other breast cancer survivors.

It felt good to compete, and it began to feel as if my life had become manageable again for the first time in a couple years. I even decided to get tattoos of nipples on my implants—and I felt whole again.

Then one day, I went to practice and couldn't get in the boat. The next thing I noticed was that I couldn't turn my head; then I couldn't swallow and started to have brain fog. The brain fog was horrible; I couldn't remember anything.

I went to the doctor with my symptoms, and they did a barrage of tests. They referred me to a rheumatologist, thinking maybe I had rheumatoid arthritis. It wasn't a condition that runs in my family. My doctors put me on rounds of a steroid medication called Prednisone. It provided no relief. I absolutely didn't know what I was going to do.

## Pink Sistas

At around the same time I was experiencing all of this, I got the opportunity to go on a retreat with Pink Sistas.

I was so excited about the retreat, but there were stairs at the retreat. And I could barely walk—how was I going to climb the stairs? What would they expect of me?

I had friends who were going to the retreat the same weekend, and I really wanted to go, too.

What was amazing is when I got to the retreat, I really didn't have to do anything except keep my feet elevated. It was such a relaxing weekend. I was able to sit in the party boat and take it easy while friends played on paddleboards and with water toys. I was able to just take it easy and didn't try to do everything. No one gave me any pushback; I could participate in what I was able to participate in.

I felt really pampered, and it took my mind off of what was happening with my body.

## Breast Implant Illness

After the retreat, I told my friend Mindy what I was experiencing with the brain fog and trouble walking. She asked if I had ever heard of Breast Implant Illness. In the past, I had heard of breast implants not being good for you, but I was unaware of any specifics. Breast Implant Illness (BII) is a group of autoimmune issues that can include chronic fatigue, fevers, brain fog, and joint pain.

I found a support group on Facebook and began to research Breast Implant Illness. By this time, I had about twenty-five different calls to the advice nurse and twelve different doctor appointments. No one could figure out what was wrong with me.

I had an EKG. At one point they thought I might be having a heart attack or stroke. I had an MRI, a CT scan, and a biopsy done on the fluid in my legs. Everything tested normal. The only abnormal finding was the inflammation I was experiencing. I met my insurance deductible for the year in just two months.

I asked my doctors if I could have BII. They said they didn't think it could be the implants, but I was given the choice to "explant," to have my implants removed.

After learning more about BII, I chose to have my implants removed; my explant surgery was on August 5, 2019. The moment they were removed, I started to feel better. I was able to walk again when I got home. It was exhilarating! I was ready to heal from the explant surgery and get back to living my life.

When the implants were removed, I was left with loose skin and fat. It was so frustrating, after everything I had been through, to look in the mirror. This is not how I imagined my body would ever look.

I wanted to scream from the rooftops and tell everyone who would listen what implants could do to you. I contacted a local news station, and they actually did a story on me and my journey with the implants.

I'm not really a private person, and I don't keep a lot of things to myself. However, after I did the interview, as I watched it, I understood that now the world would know I got my breasts cut off. It was kind of surreal, once I thought about it afterward.

I found out about an exercise class at Oregon Health Sciences University (OHSU) put on by a team of researchers. The class is for cancer patients and their significant others to exercise together. My husband and I joined the class, and it has been a good way for me to get back into working out and back into my life.

After my implants were removed, I thought I might want to try a different type of breast reconstruction called fat grafting. In fat grafting, fat tissue is removed from other parts of your body—usually your thighs, belly, and buttocks—by liposuction. The tissue is then processed into liquid and injected into the breast area to recreate the breast.

Fat grafting would create a breast where the implants were removed, and I thought it would help me to look and feel like a woman again. I did my research on fat grafting, the advantages and disadvantages, and what could go wrong.

I read that in many cases, the fat could be reabsorbed into the body and the reconstructed breast would lose volume. It could take several procedures to get results. Some of the fat injected into the breast area could die, which is called "necrosis."

Once I did my research, I chose not to get the fat grafting. There were too many disadvantages, and I wasn't willing to put my health at risk anymore.

This was the first time in my journey I felt I truly had informed consent, and I got to choose what I wanted to do.

On December 23, 2019, I went under the knife one more time. I made the choice to go completely flat. It wasn't an easy decision, but it was the right decision for me. I'm now getting used to the new me. I had my doctor write me a letter that gave me the option of working out as soon as I could.

I'm recovering from my last surgery and feeling better every day. I've met many of my neighbors through a post on Facebook asking for help with walking the dog. My neighbors have been so friendly and helpful. They started a meal train for Randy and me and have been making sure Oliver goes for regular walks until I am able to walk him again.

My girls, Tiffany and Tara, along with Randy's daughter Heather, were a major part of my healing and recovery. They were there with me every step of the way. I could not have done it without them.

It's my mission to share my story. People need to know the advantages and the disadvantages to having reconstruction after breast cancer in order to make informed decisions.

You might save your own life.

# Delo Fercho

Delo Fercho was born the fourth of six children. Growing up, she learned a great sense of frugality.

Delo was bitten by the entrepreneurial bug at an early age. She found she could make good money and there was more freedom working for herself.

Delo married Randy, the love of her life, in 2007. Randy, Delo, and Oliver, their beloved dog, live in Oregon. They have grown children and are enjoying life as empty-nesters.

After being diagnosed with breast cancer in September of 2016, Delo has made it her mission and passion to educate others on breast implant illness.

She is an active advocate in several breast cancer organizations; spreading awareness of breast implant illness, and helping survivors and their families find relief in free services.

She currently owns an embroidery business called Delo and Stitch, a food sourcing company called Ingredient Wizards, and manages an import company, Neem Tree Organics.

Delo stays in shape with CrossFit, and enjoys competing with her dragon boat team—made up entirely of breast cancer survivors.

Connect with Delo
Website: https://www.deloandstitch.com
Website: https://www.theingredientwizards.com/
Website: https://www.neemtreeorganics.com/

"Attitude
is a little thing
that makes
a big difference."

– Winston Churchill

# Finding Out I Had Cancer

The phone rang at about 6:00 pm. I had been expecting the call.

"Hi, is this Andrea? This is Doctor Germino. I performed your biopsy the other day. I just received the results."

I stopped breathing.

"We did biopsies of two areas and got similar findings. What we found is invasive ductal carcinoma. That means the cancer is malignant. We have reason to believe it will be responsive to treatment." Her voice sounded precise, but I also detected caring and a note of concern about me. "I know this is a lot of information."

I took a deep breath. And then I started writing down what she was saying in a notebook I had set out specifically for this phone call. "That's okay. I'm okay," I said. "I want you to tell me everything you can. I'm writing it down."

"We think there may be two separate masses," Doctor Germino continued. "There is one mass located at about six o'clock. It appears to be about 12 millimeters, which is 1.2 centimeters. There's another mass at about nine o'clock. That one appears to be 5.2 centimeters."

5.2 centimeters. Jesus. The thing was huge!

"Both tumors are responsive to estrogen. They are also positive for something called the HER2 protein. There are specific treatments for HER2+ tumors that we expect will be effective. The lymph node we biopsied also shows cancer."

Ouch.

"You'll be referred to a surgeon and an oncologist. They'll want to shrink the tumor first with chemotherapy. You'll go through a process called staging where they look for tumors elsewhere in the body."

Elsewhere in the body? I quickly postponed my horrified thoughts. One step at a time, Andrea.

"There are two nurse navigators who are there to guide patients through the process. One of them will give you a call, probably tomorrow.

"I know this may sound crazy to say, but if I had a big breast tumor, I'd want it to be a HER2+ tumor. There have been so many great advances in how HER2+ tumors are treated." She paused for a moment. "Do you have any questions about anything?"

I thought for a moment. "How do I know what I'm supposed to do next?"

"The nurse navigator who calls you will let you know what to do," Doctor Germino told me. "My guess is that you'll be meeting with the oncologist first, but I don't know for sure. But she'll go over all of that with you. That's her job, to guide you through the process."

We talked for a few more minutes. Doctor Germino made sure I had no more questions for the time being. Then we said goodnight, and I hung up the phone.

I sat there.

I had breast cancer, the tumor was big and there was cancer in at least one lymph node. They would be doing scans to see if I had tumors in other parts of my body.

I felt a surge of adrenaline and a tingle of fear. But I also felt a sense of calm. This was my reality. There was no disputing it. I was going to do whatever I needed to do about this, one thing at a time.

For right now, I needed to call John and let him know. John and I had met and fallen in love a little over twenty years earlier, in 1997. We were both passionate nature lovers and loved hiking and backpacking together.

At the time, I wanted more than anything to make a living

as a farmer. We purchased our farm property together in 1998.

By 2015, our relationship was falling apart. We were hosting a constant stream of live-in farm volunteers through the Worldwide Opportunities On Organic Farms (WWOOF) program. John was distancing himself from the farm more and more, while I worked harder and harder.

Things came to a head in 2015, and I told him I would leave unless he would go to counseling with me. Preparing to tell him this—and possibly to leave my life on the farm—had been excruciating. But it turned out to be worth it. We went to counseling every week for six months, and we both started to see we needed to make some big changes in how we handled ourselves and our relationship.

Now, I knew John would be there for me no matter what I was going to have to go through. I was so grateful for all that work we had done less than two years earlier. I felt certain that we could travel this road together, no matter what happened.

But right now, John was gone. Our neighbor across the river had invited us on a skiing and mountain biking vacation in Central Oregon. I hadn't gone because I needed to get the biopsy done and find out the results.

I had encouraged him to go. I knew being with people, being away from home, and getting a lot of exercise would help him.

I dialed his cell phone number.

"Hi, Puppy."

"Hi, sweetheart. Did you find anything out yet?" He sounded worried.

"Yeah, I just got a phone call from the doctor who did the biopsy. She said I have breast cancer. I have two tumors. One is about 1.2 centimeters and one is 5.2 centimeters. And there's cancer in the lymph node she biopsied too."

He was silent for a moment. "So, she just called you? You just found out?"

"Yup. I just found out. I'm glad she called me tonight, so I didn't have to wait any longer."

"That was really nice that she called you tonight."

"It is. I know." I paused. "I'm sorry, John. I know this is really hard for you, too."

"We'll get through this, Andrea. We're going to do what we need to do, and we'll get through this," he said in his calm, steady way.

"I know we are, Puppy. I know we are," I told him quietly, tears starting to run down my nose.

## Tough Times

I won't pretend it was a bed of roses. About six days after my first chemo treatment, nausea and diarrhea set in, to the point where I doubted my ability to make it through the next five chemo treatments.

A local acupuncturist who specializes in helping cancer patients gave me acupuncture designed to help my digestive system, and it seemed to help. I decided to have acupuncture once a week for the first two weeks after every chemo infusion, and I think it made a huge difference. The acupuncturist also advised me to take probiotics, fish oil, and other supplements that I think helped me a great deal while I was on chemo.

A little over a month into chemo, I was hospitalized for a blood infection that apparently started when my chemo port was placed. For the next four days, I was given intravenous vancomycin, an extremely strong antibiotic designed to kill MRSA.

The vancomycin gave me painful phlebitis and didn't get rid of the infection. The doctors finally decided to try a different antibiotic. After a couple of days, my blood work started showing a decrease in the amount of staphylococcus bacteria.

On my eighth morning there, my nurse was jubilant. She told me my blood cultures had finally been negative for forty-eight hours, which meant I got to go home.

A nurse at the Infusion Center trained me and John in how to administer the IVs at home and gave me a week's worth of supplies, which we had to refill four times.

Being on chemo and heavy-duty antibiotics at the same time was definitely no joyride for my stomach. But with the help of acupuncture treatments, smaller, more frequent meals, Britain's Got Talent videos, and probiotic supplements that I carefully took right in the middle of the eight-hour period between each antibiotic infusion, I made it through. "Yay! It's only chemo from now on!" I chortled on my last day of antibiotic infusions.

### Shock and Devastation

One of my most shocking moments came while John and I were meeting with a breast surgeon in Portland.

"Because there appear to be two tumors," she told me, "we recommend a mastectomy. And that's because there could be other cancer cells between the tumors. If we do a lumpectomy, we might not get them all."

My mouth was suddenly dry, and my heart dropped into my shoes. "I thought I would be able to have a lumpectomy," I managed to say. "Not a mastectomy."

"We always recommend a mastectomy in your situation," Doctor Naik reiterated.

After she left, I said quietly and shakily to John, "I didn't think I would have to have a mastectomy." John reached out and enfolded me in his arms.

"I don't want to have a mastectomy," I sobbed. "God damn it! I'll do it if I have to, but I don't want to have to do it! I do **not** want to have to do it!"

"Oh, Bunny," John said softly, and held me tighter while I cried.

## The Beauty of Caring

Family, friends, and neighbors came to my aid in profound, surprising ways. John's sister Lisa was on sabbatical that year and made it clear that she wanted to help in any way she could. She gave me rides home from chemotherapy and other treatments, took me shopping, and sometimes made food for me and John. Lisa and I had many long conversations in the car, getting to know each other at a depth that our busy lives had, up until now, prevented.

My friend Lorraine came to most of my chemotherapy treatments with rune cards and book passages she read to me. My neighbor Sarah, whose mom died of ovarian cancer just a few years earlier, came over with a soft pink and white blanket. She picked out the fabric especially for me and had sewn on the pink edging.

Various people made food for us when I was first home from the hospital after the blood infection, and again after my mastectomy surgery in June.

Friends from a close-knit neighborhood in south Corvallis—many of whom I had hardly seen since I stopped running my booth at the Corvallis farmers market nearly a year earlier—pruned most of our 400 blueberry bushes while I was home recovering, a time-consuming act of love which brought me to tears.

In the two decades prior to getting diagnosed, I had often been so busy working on our small farm, making jam to sell, running my weekly farmers market booth, and hosting hundreds of live-in farm volunteers, that I had not made a lot of room for friendships. And certainly not for anyone in need. I thought of lasting social connections as somewhat frivolous "extras" that could be dispensed with when I just didn't have time for them.

Being the recipient of so much love and care woke me up to a profound truth: caring about other humans is not just a nice "extra" thing to do. The care that I received was essential. I wanted to make more room in my life to care for others.

## Finding A Support Group

Chemotherapy ended in mid-April. We scheduled my mastectomy surgery for mid-June. I was grief-stricken about having to lose my breast. But my surgeon, Doctor Faddis, made it clear to me and John that he recommended a mastectomy. I had two tumors, and one of them was over five centimeters. Doctor Faddis pointed out that if he performed a lumpectomy, not only would it be difficult to make sure he was getting rid of all the cancer, but there wouldn't be a whole lot left of my breast.

I trusted Doctor Faddis. He was extremely respectful and

thorough with us, without being at all pushy. I knew he did these surgeries all the time. I didn't like his recommendation, but I would follow it.

I started looking for women who could understand what I was going through and tell me about their experience. I contacted Project H.E.R. in Corvallis. Project H.E.R. provides awareness, education, and support for all women— from the time of a breast-cancer diagnosis through survivorship. I spoke with Parker Cochran who asked about the details of my diagnosis and treatment and assigned me a mentor named Anne.

Anne talked at length on the phone with me. She had been diagnosed about five years earlier. Her diagnosis was quite similar to mine: her tumor was also large and HER2+. Her biopsy had also shown cancer in a lymph node. And she also had a mastectomy.

Anne made it clear that she was there to support me in any way she could. And she invited me to the Young Adult Cancer Survivors group (YACS) that met—and continues to meet—monthly at the Cancer Center where I was getting treated.

"Young adult? Are you sure that's okay? I'm fifty-four," I told her.

"You're so active," she told me. "I think youshould come."

Still almost completely bald from chemotherapy, still wearing a headscarf, I drove out to the Cancer Center to attend the group for the first time in May. There were eight or nine other breast cancer survivors there who had already been through treatment. Many of them had had mastectomies.

I brought out my list of questions. How much had their range of motion been impacted by the surgery? How long did it take them to recover? If they had reconstruction, how was their experience of it? If they didn't have it, why not? Were they happy with their choice?

They answered my questions and then some. I got to share my fear and my grief. I felt held and understood by women who'd been through it. They focused on my situation for most of the meeting.

## Pink Sistas

The following year, after I'd been through a mastectomy and radiation, after my last Herceptin treatment, and after my hair had grown back enough for me to have it cut for the first time, Anne emailed all the members of the YACS group to let us know that she wanted to organize a group of us to go on a retreat together in August.

Anne told us Deb Hart, who ran a nonprofit called Pink Sistas, organized the retreats. We would get to stay at Deb's floating home in the Columbia River for two nights. They would provide all our food, and we'd make jewelry and do yoga and other activities. What's more, the retreat was free.

Any woman who'd been diagnosed with breast cancer was eligible to go to one Pink Sistas retreat in her lifetime.

I knew right away I wanted to go. It was tricky figuring out a date that worked for everyone. We settled on a weekend in August. Right in the middle of blueberry U-pick season on our farm.

We have just a half-acre U-pick—not big enough to pay employees. A few years ago, I never would have left on an August weekend. But things had changed. I had changed. I found a way to make it work.

Deb welcomed us warmly and cooked for us. The first night, we shared our stories, and she told us hers. "But from now on," she said afterwards, "We're not going to talk about cancer."

The next day, a yoga instructor came and led us in a class for over an hour. A couple of instructors came and showed us how to paddleboard. We spent time relaxing. A jewelry maker came and guided us each in making two pieces of jewelry. We all went for a walk along the docks together. Deb took us for a boat ride. I felt exhilarated and satisfied from spending so much time outdoors and so much time connecting with the other women.

On the last morning of the retreat, I woke up early, picked up my journal and pen, and padded up to the top deck. Mist was rising softly off the Columbia River. I saw an egret and some ospreys. My heart was full.

“I don’t want to spend so much time worrying about me anymore,” I wrote. “I want to focus more on giving.”

Watching the water and the birds, I thought silently, “Please show me the best way for me to give.”

# Andrea Davis

Andrea Davis holds a certificate in Advanced Life Skills Coaching from Stonebrook Associated Colleges.

Andrea now offers wellness coaching to cancer patients, helping them find energy, joy and better health through research-backed strategies.

She'll be co-leading a two-day retreat for metastatic breast cancer patients with Deb Hart of Pink Sistas in November, 2020.

Andrea was diagnosed with Stage 3 triple-positive breast cancer in December 2017 and had chemotherapy, a mastectomy, and radiation.

She also used multiple holistic strategies to fight her cancer, including diet, exercise, supplements, meditation, and the priceless support of many family members and friends.

There's no evidence of cancer in her body today.

Andrea loves gardening, walking and hiking, making music and singing, and spending time with friends and family.

She grows half an acre of U-pick blueberries on her organic farm in Kings Valley, a rural community in western Oregon where she's lived for more than 21 years with her partner, John Madsen.

Connect with Andrea
Email: andrea@andreadaviscancercoaching.com
Website: https://andreadaviscancercoaching.com/

# Life is better

# in Pink

Cotton candy, lips, balloons,
little presents with big bows,
jammies, diamonds, champagne,
fluffy clouds at sunset, cupcakes,
sweet peas, roses and jasmine.

# Every Life Has a Story

Today I will share mine. My name is Tami Marie Starkey. I am forty-two years old and a survivor of metastasized breast cancer.

My personal journey with cancer started long before I was actually diagnosed. It all began when I was in the third grade and my beloved Aunt Ronda was first diagnosed at the age of thirty-five.

I am not sure how much you really know about sickness and disease at that age, but I do remember being deathly afraid of it. To watch my aunt become ill from chemo and radiation and lose her hair and breast really did something to me. She continued to battle cancer for the next six years; unfortunately, she succumbed to the disease at the age of forty-one.

Aunt Ronda was not only a teacher, mentor, and inspiration to me, but to hundreds of others. Her love and devotion for children was like none other. She would travel up to sixty miles per day from her home in Corbett to where she taught grade school at West Tualatin View Elementary.

If a child was struggling in school, she would encourage them to be the best that they can be. In order to entice her students to strive academically, she would offer a family pet or a weekend retreat to her farm.

As if losing my sweet aunt wasn't enough, history repeated itself with my precious mother Patty. At age fifty-five, her doctor found a lump in her breast during her yearly Papanicolaou. After her diagnosis, I knew it would not be if, but when, that I, too, would develop breast cancer.

I am ecstatic to announce that my mother is still with us today. She will be ten years cancer-free this year. She also shared a love and devotion for children. She taught, mentored, and inspired me and hundreds of children at Corbett Grade School. She is strong, supportive, caring, loving, and kind. I am honored and blessed to call her mine! Please continue to pray that she will remain healthy and cancer-free for many more years to come.

Because of my family history and having large breasts, I

started getting mammograms at age thirty. I had dense tissue, which increases your risk of cancer and makes it more difficult to interpret the mammogram.

Cancer and dense tissue are both white, which makes it hard to detect the cancer—like trying to find a polar bear in a blizzard.

Those facts were all that I needed; I sent in a request for a prophylactic mastectomy. The doctor couldn't believe that I was willing to go through a major surgery if I didn't have the disease. According to his statistical data, I had only an 18% chance of having cancer. However, he and his data were both wrong. The dye-injected MRI prior to my procedure showed that I did in fact have cancer.

Thinking back and going through my after-visit summaries, I also had warning signs such as dimpling in my skin and an internal itching/burning sensation that I could not scratch. If you have or experienced either of these symptoms, please get to your doctor right away. Early detection is the key to survival.

If I can give you one piece of advice, it is this: listen to your body, speak up when something doesn't feel right, and be your own advocate. You are the only one who truly knows how you feel. Get a second opinion if your concerns are overlooked or swept under the rug like mine were. This will give not only peace of mind but confirmation of the diagnosis.

## Pink Sistas

A good support system is a must! Surround yourself with positive and loving people. It made a huge difference in how I felt, what I thought, and how I acted.

I was fortunate to attend the Pink Sistas winter retreat at Government Camp in November 2019. We spent the weekend meditating, making art with trinkets and buttons, and decorating cookies.

The retreat not only renewed my heart and soul, it connected me with some amazing, beautiful and strong women from near and far. Our paths may have never crossed had it not been for Deb Hart and the Pink Sistas retreat.

## Gratitude

I would like to personally thank those who have been a major part in my journey. They are the reason that I made it through the darkest days of my life. I am and forever will be thankful for each and every one of you!

The Lord, for dying on the cross so we can have everlasting life, giving me the opportunity to see another day and providing me with the strength and courage to overcome cancer. He has been my rock and foundation in which I can stand firm.

Nick Clark, for being the handsome cowboy who rode in on a white horse while I was battling a storm within myself during my diagnosis. For showing me chivalry isn't dead:

opening doors, calling my father to ask if you could take me on a date, bringing flowers to my mother and me, and riding at Winchester.

My parents Robert James Jr and Patty Marie Loose, who truly are the World's Greatest! You lead by example—you taught me to be respectful, empathetic, attentive, disciplined, honest, independent, supportive, caring, loving, and kind. Thank you for making me who I am today.

My daughters Hailey Lynn and Hannah Marie Starkey. While you are my biggest fans, supporters, and cheer leaders, you are also my heroes. You have endured so much suffering and loss in your short little lives yet have persevered with dignity and grace. You are loved for the little girls you were, and the special women you have become. I love you the most, my Hailey Bug and Hannah Banana. I thank God for giving me you!

My siblings Jennifer Fowler, Stephanie Paul, and Robert Loose, for being my best friends, reminding me that "we got this," for always having my back, for the many childhood memories and for being the *best* Aunties and Uncle to my girls.

Carol Cook, for saving my life not only physically, but mentally as well. You really are my angel on earth! I have greatly enjoyed our time together at church and Bible study, coffee dates, symphonies, berry picking, making cookies, and talking for hours.

Mary Zogg, for giving me peace and comfort, hope and inspiration by showing me that reconstruction surgery can be beautiful. I have greatly enjoyed our time together at church, Bible study, and on walkabouts. Thank you for introducing me to your sweet friend Deb Hart.

Deb Hart, for being the fearless leader and founder of Pink Sistas. Your weekend retreat gave me hope, encouragement and new friendships I will cherish for the rest of my life. You are a life-saver, game changer and an inspiration to so many. I appreciate all you do!

Bruce Ray Evans, for loving me when I didn't want to love myself, giving me a key to your home and to your heart, planting pink flowers, dancing in the living room, singing silly songs while playing the guitar, candle lit dinners, and lots of wine.

While cancer has taken many personal things from me and those that I love most, it also gave me many things to be grateful for. I grew spiritually by drawing closer to God. I learned to give thanks and praise even in the valley. It taught me that each day truly is a gift and to not take it for granted.

Thank you for taking the time to read my chapter. May the good Lord bless you and keep you!

# Tami Starkey

Tami Marie Starkey is a loving mother, daughter, sister and aunt.

Tami's two beautiful daughters, are her greatest accomplishment; they are her pride and joy.

Tami is a native Oregonian who loves Jesus, her family and friends. She is a Christian with morals, values, self-respect and worth. She prays to have eyes that see the best in people, a forgiving heart and a faithful soul. She loves unconditionally, gives without reason and cares for others without expectation.

Despite experiencing many losses throughout her lifetime, she remains thankful for the past, hopeful for the present and optimistic for the future.

Connect with Tami
Facebook: Tami Starkey

You are

Powerful,

Beautiful,

Brilliant

&

Brave

# The Many Revelations of the Big 'C'

I'm in the room, you know the one, all survivors do. It is white with a bed and an ultrasound machine. In the middle of this room, one of the ceiling panels has been switched out with a photo installation. The scene has fluffy clouds and blue skies looking over a river with some small boats in it.

More importantly, this is the room where my world would soon be turned upside down.

When I changed into my gown on that warm day in late September, I thought to myself how nice it must be for those receiving bad news to have something comforting to look at. I remember being that person as I looked up at the panel and heard the radiologist say they believed my suspicious lump was cancer.

All I could do in that moment was fixate on the word *cancer* and surrender to the needle now pointed in my direction plunging me and the life I once knew into a new trajectory.

My life prior to that day, as my mother would say, was a charmed one. A single, well-educated, outgoing, thirty-three-year-old with a thriving career, I was in excellent health as an organic eater, fitness fanatic, and a near daily meditator. Aside from enjoying a glass of wine and having a sweet tooth, I was by most standards, living a healthy lifestyle.

Unlike many breast cancer symptoms, pain is what drew me to the lump. I went to favor my left breast one summer morning that previous August and felt the small nodular.

This is new, I thought. I convinced myself that it was probably a harmless cyst, like the one I had experienced in my late teens. Given my age, the thought that my lump could be cancer was the last thing on my mind. As a result, I ignored it and told myself that it would go away just like the other cyst had in the past. Luckily, the slight twinge persisted over the next few weeks.

Intuitively, I knew the pain was telling me something wasn't right. By mid-September, I had made an appointment with my primary care physician, setting my mentioned path above into motion.

In the few agonizing days it took to get my biopsy results back, fear consumed me. In a free fall of my emotions and desperate to grasp onto any control, I began to research. Nearly manic, I had to know everything about breast cancer, from the best prognosis to the worst, assessing all the various treatment options and outcomes for each. In those few days everything that I'd read terrified me. The reality that my life could significantly change had set in.

Faced with the immediacy of my death, all the fears and insecurities that I had had prior to my diagnosis felt menial in comparison. Feeling at my most vulnerable, I began to question my mortality and specifically if I would die from this disease. I clung to my phone as I broke the news to my family and close friends. I knew I was going to need all the support I could get in order to survive what was ahead of me.

When my biopsy results came in, I was initially told that my lump was Ductal Carcinoma in situ (DCIS), which is noninvasive pre-cancer. At the time, this was a huge relief, but it was short lived. Unfortunately, after my first surgery, a lumpectomy, the pathology results discovered that in the center of my 1.9 cm DCIS tumor, was 5 mm of invasive cancer.

Furthermore, the pathology report indicated the Grade 3 tumor was triple positive (ER+/PR+/HER2+). This meant another surgery to remove more breast tissue and lymph nodes, but fortunately would leave my breast intact.

Just prior to that second procedure, I received a call from my surgeon. Even though I was upstaged to T1A, she indicated that upon review of my case, the oncology team would be recommending chemotherapy and targeted therapy.

With this critical information, I reluctantly agreed to have a port catheter placed just below my right collar bone. When I thought of chemotherapy, my mind could only think about the extremely scary side effect (severe nausea, vomiting, rapid weight and hair loss) dramatized in movies and television. In this reflection, all of my opinions of chemotherapy and cancer treatments were rooted in these fears. Naturally, I dreaded and resisted the idea that I would need conventional treatments. My anxiety heightened when I thought about receiving the *poison.*

I obsessed about all the things that could go wrong during the treatment process. I feared all of the harsh side effects, but also knew the treatments would destroy cancer cells. At a stalemate, I made a promise to myself I would not let my fears of treatment stop me from a recommended plan, especially if it could save my life.

During the first appointment with my oncologist, I was surprised to hear how far cancer treatment had come. I learned there were different types of chemotherapy and cancer targeting treatments, many of which were tolerable enough for patients to continue with their daily routines.

Breast radiation was unlikely to make me severely ill, nor would it contribute to more head-hair loss.

Lastly, my oncologist informed me of a process called cold capping, where many cancer patients were successfully maintaining more than half of their hair while undergoing chemotherapy!

This appointment was a pivotal turning point for me. It is important for me to acknowledge that not every plan and response to treatment is the same, however, I realized that much of my knowledge of chemotherapy and other cancer treatments were completely uninformed and misguided. Especially since I would receive a tolerable course of twelve weeks of paclitaxel, eighteen rounds of targeted therapy, and short-course radiation.

Instead of feeling powerless, my treatment plan gave me hope. For the first time since my diagnosis, I felt a sense of control over my body.

Feeling empowered, I sprang into action and put several things in place a few weeks before my first infusion. I saw a naturopathic doctor who specialized in cancer care and recommended many complementing remedies (confirming that it would not interfere with conventional treatment). I strictly adhered to a ketogenic diet and started experimenting with intermittent fasting. Most excitingly, I ordered a cold cap system, in an attempt to save my hair! Then, I rallied up my family and friends to assist me on each infusion day that coincided with a weekend. With all of the preparation, I was ready to embrace my biggest fear in this journey.

Since I was in my early thirties and single, the subject of preserving my fertility weighed heavily on my mind and heart. I knew in my twenties that I wanted to be a mother someday. I often daydreamed of a little girl whose features and mannerisms resembled my own. However, my circumstances up to my diagnosis hadn't yet presented the opportunity.

After discussing the topic with my oncologist, I opted to get a monthly injection, which would protect my reproductive system during treatment. I will continue to remain on this injection, in addition to an oral aromatase inhibitor, until my five-year marker, all in the hopes that my fertility will return and to prevent the chance of recurrence.

Infusion days, to my surprise, weren't nearly as scary as I had built them up to be. Other than a slight poke to access my port, the actual infusions themselves were painless and uneventful. Additionally, with the help of pre-treatment medications and acupuncture, I never had to hug the porcelain throne. Also, the cold caps proved to be a huge success, as I ended my last chemotherapy infusion with a full head of hair!

Now, I don't want to diminish the side effects of chemotherapy for anyone. The experience is different for each patient. I still suffered many unpleasant ones. However, as each week passed without a major health incident, I began to grow more confident and less fearful of the treatment process.

As strange as it sounds, what I valued most while going through cancer treatments was how much closer it brought me to my family and friends. I fondly reflect back as each loved one took turns meticulously strapping my cold cap onto my head during infusion days. They'd tuck me in on the couch to watch shows or play games, as we enjoyed the keto-approved meals they had prepared for me.

From the support of my employer and coworkers rooting me on, to all the messages of well wishes, I strongly attribute all of those efforts to the acceleration of my healing, both physically and emotionally.

Throughout the year of my journey, a string of unfortunate events unfolded within my family. Two of my grandparents passed away. My stepmother, a metastatic Stage 4 breast cancer survivor herself, had a cancerous tumor return. Perhaps the most shocking, my maternal grandmother was also diagnosed with breast cancer. Her tumor was in the same breast and quadrant as mine. Despite shared similarities, we both tested negative for any BRCA mutations. I'm happy to share that they have both recovered.

My cancer alone would have been challenging enough, but to experience the loss of loved ones and also to watch those you care about suffer from the same disease was more crisis than anyone typically experiences in the span of a year.

## Pink Sistas

As I navigated through these moments of hardship, I knew that at some point I wanted to connect to a group of survivors in some way. When you enter the world of disease, you enter into a community of people that get it. They are there for you in a way only the sick and surviving can be. It was exactly what I needed at just the right time when my former college roommate's mother connected me to Pink Sistas for a no-cost weekend retreat with other survivors of breast cancer.

When I arrived at the retreat home on the river, the gracious Pink Sistas founder greeted me and ensured that I felt at ease. After meeting each survivor and having one of the many delicious meals made for us, we gathered and shared our stories. Providing tips and advice on the remedies that worked for our treated bodies. Through the weekend I didn't get any puzzled looks when I frantically stripped off layers of clothing during a hot flash. I could awkwardly flop and flail without any judgement during all the activities (yoga, water sports, boat rides). We would even reach a place of sacred trust to show each other the scars and outcomes from our surgeries. In our shared camaraderie of survivorship, we understood one another and could be our most authentic selves.

The Pink Sistas weekend gave me the time to reflect on the enormity of what I endured since the day of my diagnosis.

## Revelations

As this chapter is so titled, I have had many revelations while on this journey, many of which you have just read. Cancer undoubtedly has been the most challenging and difficult time of my life, but it has also been the most impactful and transformational.

I have a whole new prospective, passion, and drive in life because of this experience. I chase my dreams, leap into new challenges, and dive headfirst into every day. Evolving into one of the best and healthiest versions of myself.

Cancer has inspired me to embrace my fears and transform them into what I need to persevere in the moment. I am no longer held back by the fear of *if* or *when* I might die from this disease. I am completely unburdened, and I am finally free from cancer.

# April Everist

April Everist attended Western Oregon University and graduated with a Bachelor of Science Degree in Criminal Justice.

Professionally, April is a Victim Advocate for a law enforcement agency and assists survivors of domestic violence and sexual assault.

At the age of 33, April was faced with a shocking diagnoses of triple positive breast cancer. With the need to advocate for herself, April endured two surgeries, chemotherapy, targeted therapy, and radiation.

April balanced conventional treatment and naturopathic methods, in addition to successfully retaining her hair with cold cap therapy.

Through the support of April's medical team, family, and friends, April is now cancer free.

Connect with April :
Email: april_everist@outlook.com

the

Flower

that blooms in adversity is the most rare and beautiful of all.

# Annie's Story

This is a story all about how my life got flipped-turned upside down . . . wait, that's the opening of a song.

My name is Annie Hunnicutt and, in all seriousness, this is the story of how my life was changed forever by a few words: "Tests are back and it is breast cancer."

This is a story about hope, strength, change, and how important it is to talk to your family and know your history.

About a week after my thirty-second birthday, my husband felt a lump in my left breast. I was seen by my doctor a mere two days later. Due to my age and a lack of family history of any breast cancer, when the tumor showed up in my menstrual cycle, I was told to wait four to six weeks and see if it dissipated, as it was most likely a cyst. As someone who had some years earlier had cysts on my ovaries, this sounded like the most logical thing.

In the five weeks that passed, the tumor grew and continued to become increasingly more painful. My doctor referred me for imaging. I had an imagining appointment on August 15, 2017, my eighth wedding anniversary, and the last one I would celebrate.

The radiologist read my ultrasound before I was allowed to leave. Pulling me into a patient conference room, he said the word I had been dreading—tumor. He sent me for an immediate mammogram and told me I would need to come back in three days for a biopsy. Three days after the biopsy, I got the call.

On the morning of the big eclipse, my breast nurse navigator called with the news that I had invasive ductal carcinoma, which had spread to at least two lymph nodes. I will forever be thankful to my in-laws who we were visiting in town that morning; they kept my boys busy so we could take the phone call and figure out the next steps.

My world, which had already been falling apart, took a major blow with that phone call. I had lost my dad unexpectedly four months earlier, my marriage had been on the rocks for some time, and now I was facing a fight for my life—a fight I knew would be long and hard. I had a choice to make, a choice that would affect not only my husband Ryan and my two boys, Timothy, age four, and Gabriel, age two, but also my mom and my sister.

I could choose to allow this news to take me down the path of depression and negativity, and ultimately let it destroy me and my normal upbeat and positive personality. I chose to remain positive and fight the beast head-on.

We canceled the marriage counseling we had scheduled to start and decided that focusing on my health was going to be the best way to hit this.

The two weeks following my diagnosis was full of tests, doctor appointments, and procedures. We met my entire care team: medical oncologist, radiation oncologist, and breast surgeon. It was determined that I was at Stage 3 and we would start eight rounds of chemo after having a port placed in my chest, followed by a bilateral mastectomy, and then radiation.

We also discovered in that time that there was indeed a family history of breast cancer on my mom's side of the family. I had a hard time processing the knowledge that had we known about the family history, imaging would have been ordered clear back in June when the tumor was first discovered. I struggled with anger at the fact that it took me getting diagnosed to find out about other people in the family who had dealt with this devastating diagnosis.

My family, friends, church family, and community rallied

around us and did a lot of the heavy lifting for us, in many different forms. Groceries and care packages delivered on a regular basis. Uplifting messages. Fundraisers. They checked on us, helped with the boys, made a ton of easy-to-fix freezer meals, took me to appointments or the ER. They visited me in the hospital—most of the time just sitting with me while I slept—and surrounded us with unconditional love.

It was devastating and hard to have to miss my own sister's wedding because I did not feel well enough to travel to Las Vegas. But they understood, even agreed I shouldn't travel and set it up to be live-streamed so I could at least watch it live from home.

The first two rounds of chemo went smoothly; I just felt a bit weak and slept a lot more.

Then came the day I lost my hair. I thought I was prepared for it, it's just hair, but I wasn't. It hit me hard, and I ended up in tears as I buzzed it all off after it started coming out in large clumps.

I realized that for as long as I could remember, whenever I was feeling down on myself or needed a lift to my confidence or self-esteem, I relied on my long hair or looking pretty in an outfit. It dawned on me that my hair was gone and that while the original plan was to have implant reconstruction, my breasts would be scarred and would never be the same again. This realization hit me hard, and I struggled to keep my positive outlook.

I did two more rounds of chemo before the medication changed. The new medication, Taxol, was extremely rough. I suffered with severe bone pain and dehydration (despite drinking upwards of a gallon and a half of Pedialyte and water per day). The pain landed me in the ER several times when it was unable to be controlled at home with oral pain medications.

No longer able to drive, I was also unable to be alone with my kids due to the pain and the amount of sleep I required. Thankfully, friends and family were there at every turn to pick up the slack I could no longer handle. Finally, after my third dose of Taxol, we figured out my pain could be controlled with oral pain meds if I went into the nurse treatment room every other day for a full bag of IV fluids. With that plan we finished out my last dose on December 27, 2017.

On January 10, 2018, I had a second full body scan and it appeared the disease had been fully eradicated by the chemo. We went ahead with the treatment plan and on February 1, I had a bilateral mastectomy with expanders placed. On February 6, the pathology report came in on the breast tissue and twenty-one lymph nodes that were removed, and the chemo had indeed eradicated all disease from my body.

All seemed to be healing well until February 27, when I went to bed at 5:00 pm, not feeling well at all. I was nauseous and my whole body hurt. I had an event I desperately wanted to be at on the morning of the 28th, so I got up and took a hot bath, thinking that would help the body aches. I couldn't get out of the tub, and my sister had to drive over and help me.

She took me to the event, where I opted to use a wheelchair, and then immediately afterward took me to the ER. I had developed a massive infection around the expander on the left side. By 6:30 pm I was in surgery to remove the left expander and was put on major antibiotics. A mere three days later the same signs showed up in the right side and I was again taken into emergency surgery to remove the right expander. I spent ten days in the hospital and had to continue IV antibiotics at home for nine days.

I started radiation in April 2018. In the middle of my radiation treatment, things in my marriage came to a head and we decided to divorce. So as not to upset my treatment, I didn't move out until radiation ended.

My thirty rounds of radiation went smoothly, and I consider myself extremely lucky, as I did not have any of the bad effects I had heard so much about.

After moving out, I met with my plastic surgeon and got the news that my original plan of implant reconstruction was no longer an option after my infections. She referred me out to another surgeon who specializes in microsurgery and specifically DIEP (Deep Inferior Epigastric Artery Perforator) flap reconstruction. After meeting with him I knew this was not only the surgeon for me but the correct reconstruction choice for me.

I was quite apprehensive after hearing and seeing both good and bad testimonies of ladies who had undergone this reconstruction. I was a single mom who was looking at the prospect of dating life again. I was not just flat, but concave, with excess skin on my chest after the emergency removals of the expanders, facing a twelve- to eighteen-hour surgery that would not only leave my breasts even more scarred, but also my stomach, and there was a great possibility I would lose the nipples previous surgeons had worked hard to preserve for me.

I went through a lot of back and forth about the surgery before it was finally scheduled for December 6, 2018.

Following my separation and ultimate divorce, I had some amazing people come into my life, people who helped me decide what was going be best for me and who put me at ease about the surgery. The reconstruction went amazingly well, and I simply cannot express how thankful I am for such a great surgeon. Not only did I not lose my nipples, my scars are fading better than I expected. I developed an infection in my abdomen five weeks post-surgery that landed me back in the hospital for three days, but we caught it earlier than the previous time and it cleared up easily.

## Pink Sistas

The day of my diagnosis, my husband's aunt, after hearing about it, reached out to a friend of hers. A friend that was not only a survivor herself, but that ran a nonprofit that provides retreats for current patients and survivors. Little did I know at the time that this woman, Deb Hart, would become a wonderful friend, who would connect me to many other people I would grow to call friends and some to whom I would become incredibly close.

Right before my reconstruction surgery I had the privilege of being asked to join Deb on the first-ever Pink Sistas winter retreat up on Mt. Hood. It was exactly what I needed, when I needed it. The group of ladies I was with were fun, inspiring, and so nice. We all had a great time bonding over activities, meals, walks, and visiting.

The Pink Sistas organization has become something very near and dear to my heart and has inspired me to not only tell my story but to stretch my comfort zone and become who I am today.

## Self-Care

I am now over a year out from my reconstruction. I feel beautiful, strong, and healthy. There is always the fear the cancer will return, but I go in for my regular checks and have decided not to live my life in fear.

I have become more physically active, taking up kayaking

with my boys in the summer and working in a warehouse. I try to eat healthy, but I still enjoy cheesecake and ice cream, just in moderation now. I did not cut out drinking, but again it's in moderation, and I only have a drink as a treat every once in a while.

I learned the importance of self-care, self-love, and being an advocate for yourself, whether that be with medical staff or in friendships and relationships.

The last thing I want to touch on is something that has become my platform. Talk to one another. Talk to your family. I encourage everyone to make sure they have a solid knowledge of their family medical history, because had I known what I know now, my disease maybe could have been caught and treated before Stage 3.

Because they had to remove so many lymph nodes, I now fight with lymphedema and possibly always will. Had the cancer been diagnosed earlier—I do not blame medical staff as it made no sense at my first appointment to assume tumor or cancer—the lymph nodes wouldn't have been involved yet and this most likely wouldn't have been something I would have to deal with. So please, talk to one another, talk to your loved ones.

I have decided to live my life and enjoy it. I have learned how strong I truly am, not only physically, but mentally and emotionally. I am proud of the person I have become through this trial and journey with breast cancer.

# Annie Hunnicutt

Annie Hunnicutt is a kayaker, all around country girl and avid crafter.

Her passion is being creative and connecting with people on a real level.

Annie has a unique ability to find and connect with people in the communitees that she loves; the breast cancer community and the veteran community.

As a single mom of two small boys, she has learned the value of deep and lasting relationships and having a solid support system. Her free time is spent with her boys and those she loves and considers family.

Connect with Annie
Facebook: Annie Marie Hunnicutt

All you need is love.
But a little chocolate now and then doesn't hurt.

CHARLES M. SCHULZ

# Doing All the Right Things

I can't remember the woman I was before I got breast cancer. Based on pictures and social media posts, I was a naïve, twenty-eight-year-old mom of one, wife to my high school crush (though we didn't date until seven years after we graduated high school), and on a career track I had worked my butt off for.

I had amazing family and friends. My husband and I had dreams of a family of three. I was doing all the right things, but I was also lost, unconfident and self-deprecating. The woman I describe feels like a complete stranger to me now. How does this happen? How have I changed so much in four years that when I look at pictures of me prior to my diagnosis I barely recognize the woman looking back at me? Let me tell you.

Cancer was the last thing on my mind when I would do self-breast exams every few months; it was just something I was taught I should do once I had boobs. But in February 2016, I actually felt something for the first time in all of those years of haphazardly doing these self-breast exams. The lump was the size of a dime, hard, and my stomach fell to the shower floor the minute my fingers grazed it. I felt sick, but quickly told myself to get it together.

None of my blood relatives had breast cancer, so there was no way at twenty-eight years old I would have breast cancer. I abruptly exited the shower, grabbed my phone and googled "what does breast cancer feel like." I then spent about fifteen minutes, dripping wet, going from one site to another, changing up the way I asked the question on Google before concluding that I was in fact too young for breast cancer.

I decided I needed to push that idea to the very back of my brain because it was ridiculous! Nevertheless, each month I would continue to feel that lump get a little bit bigger, usually after my period, and each month with a sick feeling in my stomach, I would tell myself it was all in my head.

Flash forward about four months; it was Mother's Day. My husband and I woke up and were chatting in bed, when I asked him why my boobs were so lumpy. He proceeded to give me this diatribe of how muscles can sometimes feel lumpy and that I was right hand dominant. I cut him off, grabbed his hand, and informed him that my right boob is super lumpy!

The words that came next caught me so off guard that I'm surprised I didn't drive to urgent care for an exam that moment: "Danielle, that's cancer; you need to have that looked at!" The ironic thing is he was 100% joking, he had no way of knowing that it actually was cancer. I batted his hand away and told him how ridiculous that was and off we went for our Mother's Day adventure!

One of my superpowers is the ability to compartmentalize things so that they don't have the power to cripple me with anxiety, so that Mother's Day wasn't cluttered by my overactive imagination coming up with all sorts of doom and gloom, I just had fun.

Unfortunately, that night while sleeping my imagination worked overtime in my dreams, urging me to go see a doctor about this growing lump that I was now convinced was cancer. I went to work that next day, riddled with anxiety and sleeplessness. This wasn't normal, this was a pit-in-my-stomach, bad-taste-in-my-mouth, inability-to-focus type of anxiety that drove me straight to my naturopathic doctor. She was about to enter into an appointment but something in my eyes told her to see me anyway. She kindly told me she didn't think it was anything to worry about but to put us both at ease I should go have a mammogram. A referral was immediately faxed over, and I called the imaging clinic to schedule my mammogram before pulling out of her parking lot.

"Hello, scheduling. How can I help you?" said the woman at the imaging clinic

"Hi. My doctor just sent over a referral for a mammogram and I'm hoping I can get that scheduled at your next earliest opening."

"Okay, can you give me your full name and birth date?"

"Danielle Cooper, June 29, 1987."

Sighing, the woman on the line says, "I'm sorry. Why do you need to schedule a mammogram? You are too young."

Frustrated by her attitude I say, "Well, ma'am, I have a lump, so my doctor wants to have it imaged."

"Well, I can't schedule you for a mammogram." She now sounds completely exasperated by my insistence to be scheduled.

"Okay . . ." I say, with as little irritation as I can keep out of my voice, "Well, if you won't schedule me for a mammogram and I have a lump and need it imaged, what can you schedule me for?"

"Well, I guess I can schedule you for an ultrasound. Do you have a family history of breast cancer?"

"No, I don't have family history, just a lump, and you

should definitely schedule me for that ultrasound."

"I'll have to send in a request for another referral from your doctor, and if it doesn't get approved, you'll have to pay out of pocket for the ultrasound. Do you still want to schedule it?"

"Yes, your next earliest opening, please."

As I hung up from the world's most frustrating call with a scheduler, all I could think was, Am I crazy? I am young, and all the women I've ever known who had breast cancer were over forty and those very few instances I had heard of young women getting breast cancer was because of the BRCA gene. I drove home, working hard to convince myself that this would all just be something silly, it couldn't be cancer.

Three days later, on May 12, 2016, everything changed. You never expect it to be you. We watch people on TV and in books and movies get diagnosed with cancer, and it seems like such a whirlwind. You never know until you are on the receiving end of that diagnosis how unique each diagnosis and situation is.

The radiologist, who kindly told me the day of my ultrasound that she knew it was breast cancer, told me a week later, after multiple failed attempts to get an appointment that wasn't a month from the day I got my biopsy results back, that "breast cancer isn't considered an emergency." . . . **What in the actual hell**! I am twenty-eight with a one-year-old son, husband, family, career, and you are telling me my cancer can wait because it's not going to kill me today! This is, in fact, a **gosh damn emergency to me**!!

Luckily, that amazing radiologist not only spoke the truth about the lack of urgency around a breast cancer diagnosis in young women, but also advocated for me and got me in to see both a surgical and medical oncologist at Compass Oncology just two weeks later.

The entire experience from diagnosis until that first appointment was like a dream. My compartmentalization superpower paid off in dividends, because while everyone around me was losing their mind over my diagnosis, I was just ready to get busy beating cancer's ass.

Between telling close family and friends of my diagnosis, comforting people who thought it was helpful to cry or tell me stories of their "aunt" who had cancer, I shut the emotion and fear in a closet, knowing at some point I'd need to deal with it, but not being ready in that moment. I needed to be strong. I had to be strong.

The day of my first visit to Compass Oncology I was so nervous that I actually spent most of the appointmenttrying to make jokes, giggling like I was high, and walking around with a fake-ass smile. I'm sure the nurse who took my vitals had someone paged in case I lost it. I can't imagine what my husband was thinking, but I'm glad he just let me act crazy.

My surgical oncologist, Dr. De La Melena at Compass Oncology West, was so comforting, smiled and answered all of my husband's and my questions. She laughed at my ill-timed jokes and validated my fears. In honesty, it wasn't the appointment with her I was worried about, I already knew I wanted to get a double mastectomy. It was the medical oncologist I didn't want to see.

The amount of information and paperwork I was given that day was ridiculous. What was even more ridiculous was being told, not asked, when I needed to be at these appointments for my breast MRI, for my PET scan, for my port placement surgery. I believe I said, "I have a job, I don't have time for this, I have a life . . ." more times than my husband or care team could count that day. I was given the available appointment times for my pre-chemo lesson, it was the only time I was given options for appointments, with my medical oncologist's physician assistant.

My medical oncologist, Dr. Jay Andersen, gave me my treatment plan. I would receive eight rounds of chemo, every two weeks. Chemo would be split evenly between AC (Adriamycin) and Taxol. Monthly Zoladex shots to completely shut down my reproductive organs and officially put me in menopause. Four weeks after my last chemo I would have my bilateral mastectomy. I would be on five to ten years of hormone blocking medication starting immediately after my mastectomy. Six weeks of radiation, Monday through Fridays, starting roughly four weeks after my mastectomy. And six rounds of Zometa infusions every six months to reduce my risk of recurrence in my bones.

I know some cancer treatments make people very, very sick. I was lucky. I was so determined that cancer would not get to call the shots and run my life that I tracked every single side effect from that first treatment and reported back immediately to make sure if it could be helped by pre- or post-drugs, it was.

I also was avid about seeing my naturopath for fluids and vitamin infusions, like the ones people in Europe get to help their bodies recover. I also saw my acupuncturist multiple times a week to combat neuropathy, bone pain, nausea, constipation, diarrhea, etc.

I started losing my hair fifteen days after my first treatment. Two days later, I asked my husband to buzz my hair. Three days after I shaved my head, I turned twenty-nine years old and I was almost completely bald; it was rough. I had been so successful in keeping the major side effects of chemo at bay, but my naturopath and acupuncturist couldn't keep me from losing my hair.

Cancer got to take some things from me, like my hair and boobs, but I refused to let cancer dictate our life, so I asked my husband to keep his normal work hours, just as long as he could be with me on treatment days and the Sunday after treatment, which were always my hardest days. I also asked him not to quit playing in his summer adult baseball league. I wanted life to be as normal as possible.

I refused to stop working and am so glad I did, because working became a safe haven for me, a place I could escape my cancer. Don't get me wrong, it was hard. What made it easier was all the support and help from family and friends. My tribe of family, friends, and coworkers helped us in many ways over that summer. My two best friends and I would go to dinner at least once a week and one or both would stay to make sure I got our son to sleep before giving me a hug filled with so much strength and love that it would carry me into the next day.

My sister-in-law would come over at the drop of a hat to help me with our son.

My dad would take our son every Saturday to let me rest, while my husband worked or played baseball.

My coworkers rallied around me, giving me care packages and gift cards so that my husband and I could go out.

My mom continued to watch our son and keep him late if I needed to go to my naturopath or acupuncturist.

My grandparents would come take me to appointments, clean our house and take me to dinner so I could get out of the house.

My in-laws would come over to the house after they got off work to play with our son so I could sleep and rest after a long day at work.

Even with all of that help and support, that summer was undeniably hard. One of my best friends had a miscarriage almost a month after my first chemo and we spent most of July just sitting outside watching my son play in his little kiddy pool, not talking but just being there for the other.

Sometimes she and I would reflect back on a trip we'd taken at the end of April, before all of our individual issues were even a thought in our mind and laugh at those naïve stupid girls who were blissfully unaware of the pain they were about to walk into. I mean the other shoe drops at some point, right? It was a dark time.

## Pink Sistas

In the initial phase of my diagnosis, I didn't know anyone else with cancer. I didn't go to support groups, and while I followed a few young women with breast cancer on Instagram, it took me almost five months to finally meet someone my age and lived in my area, who had gone through treatments.

I was lucky to find her as she was the one that invited me to a Pink Sistas retreat. It was through that retreat that I was able to really embrace the "good" things that came with my diagnosis. Community, support, love, compassion, understanding and friendship.

Those are all things Deb Hart, founder of Pink Sistas, brings to each of her retreats.

I attended a Pink Sistas retreat a little over a year after my diagnosis. The bonds forged with the other women and the memories made are irreplaceable. Being able to find community during this time is something I will be able to hold on to for the rest of my life.

However, where there is good, there is also bad, or shall I say hard.

One of the harder parts of all this was the impact my diagnosis was having on our son. There would be evenings when he would cry for an hour after my mom dropped him off at home. For the first time, I felt as if he wanted nothing to do with me. It was hard to see the look in his eyes when I took off my hat, headscarf, or wig. It's one thing to not recognize myself in the mirror, but to know my own son didn't recognize his mama was like a thousand knives in the heart. I was told that our son wouldn't remember anything about this time and that it would have no lasting effects on him because he was too young.

I'm here to tell you that almost four years after my diagnosis our son still remembers that it made him sad and scared when I didn't have any hair and was sick.

Luckily, we've mended our relationship and he no longer looks at me with fear in his eyes, but I'm sure he will carry that trauma with him for the rest of his life.

I was blessed that by the time I had had my DIEP flap reconstruction, at the end of 2017, he was old enough to comprehend that mama had ouchies on her chest and he needed to be super careful around me.

He would help me walk to the bathroom, holding my hand the short walk from my recliner to the bathroom, and wait for me to finish before walking me back to my recliner. I truly feel that his ability to help and be present during my recovery from that surgery helped him process what was happening in a much healthier way, ultimately helping us to repair the bond so tragically broken during the year prior.

Overall, my surgeries were varying degrees of difficult. I had my bilateral mastectomy in October 2016, and other than the horrible constipation and nausea from the anesthesia, it was relatively painless, probably because my body was so beat down and numb from chemo. I decided it was a win.

I always seem to have weird complications and issues.

Here's a short list of what cropped up following my mastectomy.

My right expander had a hole in it and deflated within four hours of it being placed over the muscle during my mastectomy. This required another day in the hospital and another surgery to replace it and put a new one in.

My post-mastectomy pathology on the tumor still nestled in my breast tissue showed that I was in fact not just ER/PR+ but HER2+. This, not being captured during my biopsy back in May, was considered an anomaly. It required a complete change to my diagnosis and treatment plan and added eighteen Herceptin infusions and six Perjeta infusions over the course of the following year.

Roughly five months after my mastectomy, we found out I'm allergic to AlloDerm, the dehydrated sheet of sterile tissue that is donated from human (and sometimes animal) cadaver skin which is used to encapsulate the expanders/implants so that they don't move around in your chest, and I was diagnosed with Red Breast Syndrome.

Red Breast Syndrome occurs when the AlloDerm breaks down due to an allergy and basically turns your breast into a red-hot ball of fluid. This sealed the deal on my options. I could either have DIEP flap reconstruction or go flat.

Around eight months after my DIEP flap reconstruction, and four months after my fat grafting revision surgery, I was diagnosed with postoperative pressure ulcers on my left breast, which left me scarred and unable to continue having revision surgeries due to risk of losing my left flap tissue.

DIEP flap reconstruction is a no-nonsense surgery. It takes between twelve and sixteen hours for the surgeon to remove the tissue from your abdomen, preserving the main blood vessels that he'll use to connect it to your chest wall, and then carefully re-attach these vessels and validate that they will survive. From there it's up to five days in the hospital so that you can be monitored hourly for any blood flow issues to the flap.

You aren't allowed to lie down for eight weeks, and it gives you a scar that runs from one hipbone to the other. I don't remember much from that surgery or the recovery over the following weeks.

Again, my amazing tribe of family and friends rallied around me. My grandmother spent every day with me, making me food, keeping me company while I watched endless amounts of Netflix, and allowing our son to stay home with me during my recovery. She was definitely the MVP during that time, and I will never forget how much support she gave me.

My grandfather made countless trips up and down I-5 driving me to and from acupuncture appointments and post-ops. I'm still in awe of the support my husband, our son and I have received during these hard times and will never stop thanking God for every person that helped us get through these ridiculously hard times.

Overall, in the last four years I've evolved from being a naïve, physically healthy woman who lacked confidence and routinely trashed her body, into a sick, bald, fearful woman with Triple Positive Stage 2B breast cancer who mistrusted her body, then finally into a healthy and happy woman who has grown exponentially and has found peace and love for the body that birthed an amazing child and beat cancer.

Cancer is horrible, it truly is, but the lessons and growth I was able to take from cancer is something I cherish.

My journey with breast cancer reminds me of a tree in a forest, tall, surrounded with lush green overgrowth, perfect, seemingly full of life. Then a fire cuts through the beauty, scarring the tree and killing the overgrowth surrounding it. Man rushes in to extinguish the fire, but the damage is done, the tree is badly scarred and looks as if it may die. But it doesn't die, it continues to live, and over time, people begin to see that the fire they thought ruined and nearly killed the tree actually helped the tree to release seeds that are sprouting new and more beautiful growth. We cease mourning the scars from the fire and instead see the blessings it brought the forest.

# Danielle Cooper

Danielle Cooper is a Stage 3b triple positive breast cancer Thriver who routinely shares her journey through motherhood, breast cancer, and career ambitions on her Instagram and blog.

She was been published in Wildfire Magazine, a magazine with a focus on content written by young survivors.

Danielle is a native Oregonian and graduated from Portland State University with a degree in Business. She currently works for Daimler Trucks North America as a project manager and loves all things related to heavy duty trucking.

When she isn't working, blogging or capturing life's moments on Instagram, she is enjoying time with her husband and son, playing LEGOs, going on adventures and just relaxing at home watching movies.

Connect with Danielle:
Instagram: @coopskisses
Blog: https://www.coopskisses.com/

She leaves a little sparkle where ever she goes.

# The Vision of Pink Sistas

On August 2, 2006, when he was just twenty-two years old, we lost my son Kasey. He was a tugboat captain in Alaska and was living his dream when he passed.

Seven months after I lost Kasey, I was diagnosed with breast cancer. I had only been married for a few months before Kasey died. This new relationship was based on the fun-loving, life-of-the-party girl who was footloose and fancy-free, financially independent, and ready to live life now that the kids were gone.

I was young, healthy, and happy. I was all of these things, yet in the span of just a few months I didn't know who or what I was.

Wow. Breasts removed. Chemotherapy. Infections. I had just lost my son. To say I was not a good parent to my daughter Molly during that time would be an understatement of gross proportions. I barely had any will to get up each morning, let alone to rebuild, relive, or reconstruct. However, time marches on.

In the beginning I struggled just to get out of bed and take a shower. In the end I wrote a book, started a nonprofit, and became an inspirational speaker. In between I got new boobies. Obviously, there's more to the story!

In the train-wreck stage of things, even my new rack was a disaster. My reconstruction was okay for about five years, and then my implants encapsulated, which means scar tissue was forming and hardening around the implants. I had hunched shoulders and pain—not to mention they did not look good. So, I found a physician who claimed he could fix me right up! We had the damn things removed and replaced with the more natural lipo fat implants.

Wouldn't you know it, this too went sideways. I'll never know what really happened during that surgery, but it changed the course of my life.

Because somehow, despite a "successful" surgery, two days after arriving home my kidneys failed. Subsequently my heart also failed, although by then I was in the ICU and they were able to revive me.

Not so for the kidneys. I was sent home from the hospital after three weeks, to a life of dialysis three times a week for five hours a day. I was told there was a chance my kidneys would "kick back in." But for three months, this was my new so-called "life." The treatments were brutal, and I was ready to give up.

Like many before me I was desperate to find a reason—some purpose for all that I was going through, so I bargained and made a deal with God.

I promised if He would just get those kidneys going again, I would start a nonprofit to provide retreats for women diagnosed with breast cancer. I would write a book. I would become an inspirational speaker.

The powers-that-be must have liked those ideas, because my kidneys started working again. I wrote a book. I started a successful 501(c)3, "Pink Sistas," and I am an inspirational speaker.

The second marriage failed. (Go figure!) But the new breasts are pretty good. I was nervous about them, especially being back out on the dating scene. But I did a little research and found a woman who did breast reconstruction nipple tattoos. For me, this was the key to just possibly accepting, maybe even liking, my bosom!

The tattoos make me think I have something resembling real breasts, and in the shadowy light of intimacy, they actually feel "real."

As for my life, I got it back by giving back. I love the creativity and heart within the process of reaching out and supporting others.

I've found a man who loves me for me, and I will love him for a lifetime. Thank you, Ron, for being that man. For supporting my vision, giving me the space I needed to heal, and for loving me as I am.

## Pink Sistas

When I started my nonprofit, my vision was to provide a weekend getaway where women who have breast cancer could be pampered and wouldn't have to think about their diagnosis for a few days.

Pink Sistas retreats offer women diagnosed with breast cancer the opportunity to relax, unwind, experience new things, and to connect with others who are there or who have been there in a unique way that leaves a lifetime of memories.

Dedicated volunteers, corporate sponsorships, and fund-raising keep our nonprofit afloat so we can provide no-cost retreats to ninety women each year.

Every time I share my story, I come closer to healing my heart. Our friends and family want to be there and help, but they haven't "done the journey."

It is very different to be able to speak with someone who has suffered the same kind of challenge, the same kind of loss you are experiencing.

During treatment and surgery, our families are there for us. After this, it seems that everyone offers the "high-five," sending cards, messages, or food. Then comes a period where family and friends feel "we were there for you," but the progression continues.

As we hop out of the shower and see that our breasts are gone . . . these are the moments when the processing begins. We begin to listen to the voice in our head saying, "When is it going to come back?" "How do I get my life back together?"

When you join with other breast cancer patients, there is a sisterhood that does not end in the midst of your processing but instead reaches out a helping hand at each step as you deal with breast cancer and its aftermath. There is no judgment, only understanding.

Do not put a timeline on your own processes. Joy and happiness will return. Don't expect them to be there every moment. It's okay; this is a true hit to self-confidence and self-image. Permit yourself to be nurtured and cared for as much as your life allows.

# Deb Hart

Deb Hart is the founder of Pink Sistas, Inc.

Deb is an inspirational speaker, mother, mentor, friend, breast cancer survivor, and breast cancer survivor confidant.

Pink Sistas is a 501(c)3 non-profit corporation dedicated to raising funds for no cost retreats for women who have been diagnosed with breast cancer.

Pink Sistas retreats focus on healing after diagnosis of breast cancer through many activities: networking with others, yoga, art, kayaking and paddle boarding, social outings, and much needed rest and relaxation.

Connect with Deb
Facebook: Pink Sistas
Email: inspirationaldebhart@msn.com
Website: https://pinksistas.org

"I believe in Pink
I believe laughing
is the best calorie burner.
I believe in kissing.
Kissing a lot
I believe in being strong
when everything seems to be going wrong
I believe happy girls are the
Prettiest Girls
I beleive that
tomorrow is another day
and I believe in miracles."

- Audrey Hepburn

# My Marathon

My name is Leslie. I am a fifty-seven-year-old woman who was diagnosed in September 2018 with Invasive Lobular Carcinoma (ILC).

My husband and I had recently moved to Bend, Oregon. One night while turning over in bed I felt an unusual sensation in my right breast. It was not a palpable mass; instead, the area felt very thick. I phoned my doctor in California, and she ordered both a 3-D mammogram and an ultrasound.

I have always been diligent about staying on top of my appointments. Because of my dense breast and calcium deposits I was being monitored every six months. I told myself it was likely nothing serious. The 3-D mammogram showed nothing suspicious; the next stop was ultrasound. I told the technician to press hard, it would not hurt me. She proceeded and seemed to find something. I heard the click, click, click from the keyboard as she typed away.

We women know that means something is there. She left the room to talk with the radiologist. Minutes felt like hours. The doctor came in and sat down beside me. He let me know that there was an area that needed to be biopsied. It wasn't my first biopsy, so I tried hard not to worry. I know, easier said than done.

I had the biopsy a couple days later. They asked if they had the results back by Friday would I be willing to hear the results over the phone. I agreed.

The dreaded phone call came, and the doctor asked if it was a convenient time to talk. My heart sank. I let him know that I wanted to get my husband. We heard the news together. *Cancer*. The air was quickly being sucked out of the room as I fell into my husband's arms.

We gathered ourselves and then let him know that we had just moved to town and I didn't have a primary doctor yet. We asked him who he would recommend, and he gave us the name of his mother-in-law's surgeon. If it was good enough for her, it was good enough for me. As it would turn out, it was a great referral. Their office coordinated everything, and

I would meet with my surgeon early Monday morning. I remember going to bed that evening and feeling numb. I would softly cry, and my husband would hold me tight and whisper in my ear, "We got this." It was in the middle of that very dark night that I began to journal.

**My Marathon**

This all feels surreal. I'm in a big, blurry fog. One minute you are doing something routine and the next you are pulled into a new reality that you don't even recognize.

You hear the statistics and see the pink ribbons. Your heart aches for those women and their families but you don't see yourself hearing that news that unexpectedly makes you part of that "club."

I cry softly while my mind races past now. The "what ifs." So much is flooding in that I realize I am hearing only part of it.

I have the great fortune to have my beloved Don. He catches what I drop. He is my brave warrior who always provides safety. This, though, he cannot fix. He cannot heal me. He will stand beside me and help me gain strength. He will encourage me to scream and shout, **Bleep cancer!**

We took a walk in the forest today and I did scream. I knew that release was necessary. He celebrated my outburst.

*There will be many more to come. I am keenly aware that this is now my marathon.*

The weekend seemed so long, and here we now sat, across from my surgeon. She calmly explained the potential scenarios. An MRI was ordered for the next day. We learned that a lumpectomy would not be an option. The only card on the table was a mastectomy. Now the decisions would have to be made rather quickly. Did I want to spare my nipple? What a thing to contemplate. My left breast looked clean on all scans, yet some women choose to have the other breast removed as a precautionary measure.

That night we discussed the options in depth. My husband was fighting back the tears, and I realized this was also a loss for him. Breasts are a very sensual part of a woman's body. We had always shared a very close intimacy. How would this change us? We both cried and concluded I would have a bilateral mastectomy, nipples and all.

My plastic surgeon was in the operating room during the surgery. Expanders were put in under the muscle in my chest. Yes, it is painful. Over time this helps stretch the skin which is necessary if I wanted to have reconstruction down the line.

When I woke from the surgery, I learned that the cancer had spread to my lymph nodes and more were being tested. I was scared. Pathology came back cancer present in four of the nine lymph nodes. I knew that meant aggressive treatment was in store. Both chemo and radiation would be needed.

The decision to take the left breast proved to be a correct one, as they found a different type of breast cancer in that breast. It was Ductal Carcinoma in situ, too small to be seen on imaging. I was so thankful I listened to that inner voice and thanked my guardian angel. My second journal entry:

Evil Cells

You are not welcome in my home. You are not invited and cannot dwell here! Though you try to wreak havoc I will fight you with everything I've got.

You may be here temporarily but do not get too comfortable as I assure you, I will take this on as a mission to wipe out your cruel intention, **and** I will never, ever give you power over me.

Chemo would soon follow. The thought of my long hair coming out in big chunks terrified me. I decided that I would have my head shaved. There had to be something I could control. My husband took photos. My hairdresser first put my hair in a ponytail. *Clip*. I did not face the mirror. She then began shaving my head. He captured moments of both bravery and heartache.

I wanted to be brave and strong. Be a good sport.

Frequently people just don't know what to say. Others try and express their optimism that you might not be prepared to hear. I was having the single most sensual part of my femininity amputated along with knowing there is cancer inside of me.

The very last thing I wanted to hear was, "Everything will be okay." *Nooo*. Everything was not okay. I had those days where pushing through the chemo was all I could really muster. It was in the quiet moments where I would give myself permission to be sad while trying to be mindful that this is not a place to stay and stew for too long. I have been blessed with a loving family, amazing friends and great co-workers who have rallied around me.

My best friend heard the news over text. I was on the phone with the doctor when I got a text from her. She was waiting for the results and I knew she was eager to know. I simply put, "Buy head scarves." She knew what that meant. We would talk and cry later that night. I told her, "For heaven's sake, we just got here and now I am going to be *boobless* in Bend. Well, she took that on as her mission and had two hundred pink bracelets made, inscribed "Boobless in Bend, Leslie Kerwin Myll, 2018."

Pretty soon there were friends, family, coworkers all over the country with bright pink bracelets she had mailed out. I would get pictures from my construction team on tractors wearing the bracelets, babies, fence posts adorned with bracelets, and family across America. It really was amazing. When the 'C' word hits you, it really knocks you off your feet. There is such a structure to treatment it resembles a job. Chemotherapy was for three months. Reconstruction would follow and then twenty-five rounds of radiation. I am blessed to have had such wonderful care. I felt connected to these people who dedicate their entire lives to helping others preserve theirs.

The night before my last round of radiation I penciled this entry:

255 Days

To my body that carried me these last 255 days

...I say Thank You

To my head that had to work so hard to keep my wits when it all seemed too overwhelming

...I say Thank You

To my Heart that allowed me to feel the pain, the fear, the loss, the sadness and the truth

...I say Thank You.

To my Pride, for letting go of you that allowed me to accept help from others

...I say Thank You.

To my Eyes for giving me the opportunity to witness so many "God Moments"

...I say Thank You

To my Spirit, though beaten and battered, never broke

...I say Thank You

For the gift of my Faith that flows through me. I could not imagine this walk without you, Lord

...I say Thank You

The victory is not in winning the race but finishing it. Breast cancer does not only change your body, it also changes you.

There have been so many times I have said I was going to slow down. I was so caught up in moving forward.

Part of that grind we can so easily get caught up in. I recognize that moving forward is of no value if you don't look up and take the time to see what is around you.

There have been so many blessings with so many kind and special people. Strangers lifted my spirits. My doctors, nurses, PT, chemo and radiation techs, integrative therapy, my treasured family and friends who have all loved me through this

...I say Thank You

I was introduced to a group of women who had or were going through cancer. My physical therapist was wonderful and encouraged me to give it a try. I did and immediately was happy I followed her advice. It is in the series of connections that fate finds meaning. Through this group I made a new contact with a group called Pink Sistas.

## Pink Sistas

Pink Sistas is an organization run by a tireless soldier, Deb Hart. She has devoted her life to helping women with breast cancer in Oregon.

Being a Thriver, herself, she knows all too well the feeling of being overwhelmed by the diagnosis. I was introduced to her by another Thriver and invited to be a guest on her floating home on the Columbia River. It was to be a weekend of fella Sistas being pampered by Deb. She would make the meals, take us out on the boat, and offer yoga and jewelry classes.

It sounded too good to be true. I jumped at the chance and said yes. Later I started getting cold feet. I didn't know any of these women and had only talked to Deb over the phone. I was chickening out but knew I had to push myself outside of my comfort level.

I arranged to go with another lady from Bend. We would share a three-hour drive together. By the time we got there I had a new friend.

It was a remarkable weekend. Six of us plus Deb would share our stories and laugh and cry together. Encourage and listen. Some would open up and cry that they had not known how to talk about it. Just sharing with other women who truly know is so comforting.

We all said our goodbyes that Sunday afternoon, all of us promising to keep in touch. The night I got home I reflected on the weekend and how powerful it was. We need each other in a way that our friends and family can't accommodate.

### Stairs

We all took the same path up those stairs. Most of us, apprehensive. What awaits us? The reality is that anytime you bring strangers together it is a bit intimidating. What does this weekend even look like? None of us knew and what unfolded was purely organic.

You cannot script this journey. It must be felt and lived to be appreciated. This weekend represented putting down my warrior armor and allowing myself to be vulnerable. To be with women who understand.

It has truly been an honor to be part of this experience, one that will continue to grow. Deb has given us a much bigger gift than this incredible weekend. She has given us a shared bond.

I will forever be grateful I took those steps up those stairs and met all of you beautiful, strong, kind and inspiring women.

I am so happy we have a Pink Sistas get-together every few weeks. We have such a profound and special bond. We support one another as we go through our scans, our scars and our scares.

## Gratitude

This past year has been filled with so many emotions. My perspective has certainly changed. Time becomes more precious, and how I choose to spend it more meaningful.

The bounce back from cancer is crude. Fortunately, there is incredible support in the breast cancer community. I see a sea of soldiers by my side. Their encouragement has meant the world to me.

My goal is to help others who are newly diagnosed while also bringing attention to Invasive Lobular Carcinoma. When I was diagnosed, I had no idea there were different kinds of breast cancer. Less than ten percent of all cases are ILC. The way this cancer presents itself makes it very difficult to detect on a mammogram, therefore it is often missed altogether. It is a sneaky cancer; thus, women with dense breasts *must* have an ultrasound.

I am thrilled to be in remission. Because my cancer is estrogen/progesterone positive, I must take a daily aromatase inhibitor, basically a chemo drug. I don't like the drug's side effects, but it is critical to my survival.

My heart is filled with gratitude and I celebrate every day.

Life's journey is a mystery, one that I continue to reflect on, grow, and learn from.

# Leslie Kerwin Myll

Leslie Kerwin Myll was born and raised in Southern California. She earned her BS from Chapman University and began her career with a Fortune 100 company.

Her love of design and real estate pulled her in a new direction where she established a long career in real estate with a builder/developer.

While traveling with her husband to Bend, Oregon, they realized this was the place they wanted to call home. With their children grown they took a leap and made the move.

Within weeks of moving she was diagnosed with invasive lobular carcinoma (ILC). "What, there is more than one kind of breast cancer?"

She quickly learned that ILC requires a different screening protocol and ultrasound is necessary for women with fibrocystic and dense breast. She is an advocate for educating women of this important information because too often ILC is found at a more advanced stage.

Leslie is a licensed Oregon Broker and is excited about her new future.

Connect with Leslie:
Email: Leslie@fredrealestate.com
Cell: 541-604-0197

Interiors by Leslie
Email: Gustologan@gmail.com
Cell: 541-699-2636

# Survivor

[ ser-vahy-ver ]

Determined

Defiant

Strong

Never Gives Up

# My Change of Plans

I want to believe what happens to us, our circumstances, actions, chances, are all a part of our journey from above. My belief was always to take this 2011 "situation" and find out what I was supposed to be learning or growing from.

As I write my story today, I find myself looking backward again, not knowing what to put on paper that may make someone else stronger or, at the very least, not as scared of what could come.

As my daughter told me that evening, "Mom, you have had to change so many things since the first time you had cancer. You helped us to believe there is good in every situation even if the change was going to be difficult." I wanted my girls to know that even when life goes nothing like what you had planned, I really believed there are gifts you can find along the journey you must go through.

I have always had a strong career, fought and competed for success. As a Field Training Specialist, I worked hard to inspire others, provide motivation to embrace change:

*Change is hard but will give you courage.*
*Courage gives your strength and confidence.*
*These beliefs were in my nature from as young*
*as I could remember*
*"Be yourself, no one else is qualified."*

My first encounter with death and illness was when my father passed at forty-eight years of age. I was just twenty-two and didn't get to say goodbye. He had a stroke and never regained consciousness. That was a turning point for me, not only to try to be strong for my mother, but to know how to go on without my dad, who is never going to see my children.

Facing the reality that we will all go someday and not saying goodbye changed me.

As my heart for giving and helping others grew, my kindness grew, and I began giving to others, by way of knowing they are worth something.

I met the love of my life in 1990 and we had two beautiful girls over the next ten years. After growing careers and settling into our family life, the life changes once again came at a force we did not see.

## The First Diagnosis

I was always told I had lumpy and dense breasts. I had to be diligent in checking and my doctor had me on yearly screenings.

Even with the yearly checks, in the summer of 2011, I looked up at the mirror and my left breast was shrunk with a large vein exposed. My husband and I headed to the doctor. The mammogram showed nothing again, but the ultrasound said it all. After a very painful biopsy, I was diagnosed with Stage 4 Breast Cancer.

Stage 4.

Stage 4.

I called the American Cancer Society and just lost it. I was dying, and Jill was my angel on the other end of the line who somehow brought me back to some sort of acceptance—but now how to take back control?

My mind kept going to work, feeling I would be disappointing them. You see, I was selected to be a special trainer for my company and my managers. I chose to put off immediate surgery to deliver training in five states and be that giver before surgery put me out. *Ha*! Did I think I had it all figured out. . . .!

It was flurry of doctor appointments, meeting with the

team of surgeons, oncology, radiation doc, and my plastic surgeon. No one in my family has had breast cancer. To be so aggressive, and my mammograms not catching it during yearly visits kept me sad and angry. Two cysts, one 10 cm and the other 3 cm.

I was given a choice to have the double mastectomy or just remove the one. This is where I was tested.

I was forty-seven years young and still "cute." Did my husband want one boob? I prayed and prayed. An instinct told me to get both off now.

What an instinct God led me to, the second one did have cancer, I win this one! Everyone had missed it, which was alarming. Thirty-two lymph nodes later, taken from the left side, with twenty-four of them carrying cancer, I was downgraded to Stage 3C, as it did not leave the chest wall. I win again!!

At that point I didn't care what they called it; I was in bad shape. My underarm had a softball in it (scar tissue). I couldn't lift my left arm all the way and had braiding throughout my arm. My plastic surgeon said the general surgeon took so much skin, I was left unable to have breast implants or any other surgery to get my figure back as a "woman."

The next few months were some of the most difficult of my life, but my friends rallied and new friends I met in my journey brought me so many gifts—organizing meals, bringing groceries, and cleaning my house. Seeing my hairdresser sobbing as she helped me shave my head. There were other gifts as well, too many to mention.

I began to reach out to whomever could relate to my *big question*—the sleeve.

Why was it recommended to wear every day?

Did anyone know how uncomfortable and ugly this thing was?

I read an article about a Canadian doctor that started a dragon boat team for breast cancer survivors with lymphedema. I found these women did not wear their sleeves every day as long as they practiced on the water in a dragon boat.

I told my good friend I wanted to move to Canada, and she promptly introduced me to the Pink Phoenix Dragon Boat Team which led me to an incredible gift—a platform connecting to others, sharing experiences, exercising, and feeling valued. Everyone on the team had been touched by breast cancer.

I was told it would be good to connect with others on the team, so I went on a lot of "blind dates" with these women, which brought me new friends and new perspectives on life. I couldn't sit around and mourn with these women; they had to be strong and not want to give up. Keep fighting, I was told, so I did.

One of the biggest gifts throughout this whole cancer

journey was meeting Sandy, another newbie on the team. We became fast friends.

## Pink Sistas

I then met Deb Hart. She is the founder of Pink Sistas, a nonprofit for women diagnosed with breast cancer. They provide retreats at no cost where you can escape for a weekend retreat on the water to rest and rejuvenate. We (Vancouver Pinks) took Sandy to Deb and spent a retreat weekend together.

Deb was another gift to me because not only does she run a nonprofit, but she is a hospice nurse and sat with Sandy at the end.

Deb and I became great friends. I became a big part of Pink Sistas and found a new purpose.

## Next Steps

In 2013 it was time to find my body again. Because I don't quit or accept easily, I found an unbelievable breast center in New Orleans with stellar recommendations and doctors with experience in lymph node dissections. Another journey to New Orleans, fourteen hours of surgery, and I had a chest again—and the "softball" removed from my armpit.

Now it was time to recover and figure out my next steps. I had a substantial career that just stopped when I got cancer. I went back to work part-time and then eventually full-time. I couldn't do it, my body said no.

Five years later, I am successful in a new career in real estate. I can help people and give of myself and my time and money to charities.

## Being Diagnosed With MBC

As a breast cancer dragon boat team, we had the opportunity to compete at the International Breast Cancer Participatory Event (Racing) in Florence, Italy, in 2018.

As I prepared my body to be chosen for the team, I started having pain in my lower back and right leg during practices. I chalked it up to the workout routine, stress, and work hours, but no matter what I tried, the pain remained. My next pain came in my front ribs, a bump appeared. I was slightly worried but not enough to go get checked.

Skip ahead to Italy. We raced hard all weekend then early in July. That Monday in the hotel room, I could not get out of bed, my back hurt so bad.

Once you've had cancer, you worry that every little ache and pain is a recurrence. And you worry that your doctor thinks you're a hypochondriac. I was sure that when I called my oncologist to ask about my rib and back pain, she would tell me I was overreacting. Instead, she scheduled me for imaging.

Within twenty-four hours I was imaged, and within twelve hours I had the news. The news hit me as if the wind was knocked out of me.

The words all seemed grim. And I was right: when I looked them up, words like "incurable," "metastasis," and "terminal" were what I saw. I was going to have to call my daughters. But how do I tell them I am going to die—I have not seen them graduate, get married, or have a family. One daughter is just eighteen, and the other so strong at twenty-three.

That afternoon, I kept saying "I am going to die" and reliving the image of my husband in the chair, grey and crying. I sobbed in his arms that night after an argument.

How could all this be happening just seven years from the first diagnosis. All I had wanted was an ordinary life, and to retire together with my husband of twenty-seven years, watching the waves somewhere. I am scared this will not happen for us.

There are cycles to living with metastatic breast cancer. Of course, first comes fear, sadness, mourning, then gratefulness, appreciation, acceptance, even tedium. And denial. Most people feel denial at the beginning, "This can't be happening to me" or "I'm just eating wrong, I can fix it with flax seeds and cannabis." (You can't.)

## My Final Change of Plans

There is no final with MBC.

The last change for now is for me to live a life, find a new normal, and to embrace the changes. No longer able to do what I love—paddling, four-wheeling, running, working long hours—I am changing my identity to fit my new normal.

My husband once said to me, "We can't do those things anymore, because you are always in pain." That hurt to hear but made me want to change how I was coming across to him. My family is going through cancer, too. A counselor told me it was okay to grieve my previous life before cancer. "Just don't let it be the reason you do not find anything else to make you happy."

I want to continue to provide inspiration to family, friends, coworkers, future clients. I want to live up to how people see me:

"Your open heart, friendly smile, drive, and constant caring about others inspires me. The total support you give your daughters and friends is non-stop and very appreciated."

"While going through great adversity Robin showed incredible courage. She continued to show how much she cares about her clients and her team by passionately going above and beyond what is expected for all of us."

Because I am a fighter and still a "survivor," with so many of my friends and clients behind me, that next journey is living with MBC. While being in treatment I can and will live life—a quality life.

The reality of being faced with choosing between life or

death: I will not take negative opinions under consideration. As I have learned, being faced with an actual problem is a lot different than imagining it. There are very few who do not want the precious time they have and will give it up readily. That, of course, is not who I am.

I am Robin Ray-Rutherford, fifty-five years young.

## Looking for my new normal

"Strong women aren't simply born. They are made by the storms they walk through. From the pain, mistakes, and heartache we achieve pride and strength. I don't know who needs to see this today. Or yesterday. Someone you know might get this phone call tomorrow. Show them what strength looks like. Let them know they are not alone. Stand by them as they kick this like the warrior they are!"

Thank you to Annette Johnson for allowing me to capture the pain, beauty, and bravery it took to spread this message. Prayers to you and our loved ones who stand strong behind us as we fight!

# Robin Ray-Rutherford

Robin Ray-Rutherford started working at the age of twelve with patrons of her parent's bakery.

She grew up believing service is not a definition but a state of mind.

Paying attention to the needs of others, listening, and being genuine. A willingness to serve that motivates you to keep doing better.

A former Navy veteran, Robin maintains the highest level of attention to detail. She is passionate about our senior and veteran communities and ensures these groups are treated with kindness and respect.

As a licensed real estate agent, her mission and driving force are to provide guidance, consistent communication, and support to her clients. Real Estate is a relationship not a transaction, and Robin values every one of those relationships.

Robin puts her heart into everything she does and works with a high degree of integrity. Volunteering her time with breast cancer survivors, she works with Pink Sistas Inc., and with her Dragon Boat team, Pink Phoenix.

Robin donates a portion of her commissions to one of five charities she supports or to a non-profit of choice her client is passionate about.

Connect with Robin:
Email: HomesbyRobinR@gmail.com
Website: HomeswithRobin.com
Cell: (360) 901-0961

Inspire
hope
Dream
believe

# Is This What I Think It Is?

It was Rose City Comic Con Weekend in Portland, a big deal in my house. My husband and son are both comic book geeks. We all went down to the Convention Center for the Con that Sunday, January 25, 2015. I was feeling kind of off all day. You know the feeling, like you might be coming down with a small virus or something. I brushed it off as nothing and tried to enjoy the day with my family.

The next morning though, as I was getting ready for work, I put my bra on and stuck my hand down the side of my right boob to adjust it in the bra (as I'm sure we've all done a time or two). I will never forget it. I felt a lump. Not just a tiny little pea sized lump. This lump was about the size of a nickel and quite noticeable to the touch. When did this show up? Why had I not felt this before? Is this really what I think it is?

I decided to just go on with my day and try not to think too much about it until I got home from work. That's when I had my husband come up to our room and feel it. I first had him feel the left breast, then the right. He looked at me and said, "Oh, that's not right. You need to call the doctor tomorrow and have that checked." That's when the fear really started to kick in. My stomach was turning, I didn't sleep all night, I just couldn't get my brain to stop going to the worst outcome.

Tuesday morning, January 27, 2015. I went to work, never told a single soul what I had found, and waited for my doctor's office to open so I could call and get an appointment to be seen. I found an empty board room and closed the door. I nervously dialed and waited for the front desk to answer. When she did finally answer, I told her who I was, who my doctor was and that I had found a lump in my right breast. She asked if I could be in the office in twenty minutes.

"Of course!"

I told a coworker I had an emergency appointment and would be back, and out the door I went. I was trying so hard not to cry the whole drive to the doctor's office. Once there, they put me in an exam room, had me put on a gown, and then the doctor and his nurse both came in for the exam. I love my doctor . . . he's amazing. He was so calm about the whole thing. He had me lay back with my arm over my head, closed his eyes and started his exam on the left boob. He kept his eyes closed and moved over to the right boob.

As soon as his fingers came to the lump, his eyes opened. He looked at me and said, "That's it, isn't it?" I answered, "Yes." He assured me that it was probably nothing but wanted to send me in for a mammogram—it had been two years since I'd had one—to be sure. I had my mammogram two days later. They didn't like what they saw, so I was then scheduled for a biopsy.

Tuesday, February 3, 2015. Today was biopsy day. I was terrified, to say the least! My husband went with me for support, the first of many appointments he'd be attending with me. He was able to be in the room with me during the biopsy. I remember being so grateful for that. He held my hand. I cried. He gently wiped my tears. They took a biopsy of the lump on my breast, as well as an inflamed lymph node under my right armpit. They placed tiny titanium markers at the same time. They sent me home with an ice pack under my arm, advised me to take some Tylenol for the pain and said the doctor would call with the results. Then came the waiting game. The worst game *ever*!!

Friday, February 6, 2015. The answer was in. I got the call from my doctor that evening. I'll never forget it. He sounded devastated. "I am so sorry to have to tell you this, but the biopsy results came back showing that you have metastatic, poorly-differentiated carcinoma. It's triple negative breast cancer, and it's also in the lymph node that was biopsied."

I was forty-three years old. My husband and nineteen-year-old son sat on the couch in the living room watching my face while I got this news, all the while wondering what the doctor was telling me. I wrote it all down, thanked the doctor, went and sat on the couch with my husband and son and cried, while telling them, "I have cancer." My entire world had just changed, and I had no idea how big of an impact it was going to have on my life, on our life, going forward. This was the day the whirlwind truly started.

I was blessed with a doctor who had connections to some of the most amazing and best doctors in the Portland area. The ball was rolling, and it was rolling quick! I met with my surgical oncologist, my medical oncologist and the genetics counselor the very next week. We decided to have a port placed so as to save my veins. My port was placed on February 18, 2015, and I started my first of eight ACT chemo infusions on February 20, 2015. Everything was happening so fast, I felt as if my head was up in the clouds and I was watching my life happen from afar.

Chemo sucked . . . it truly sucked. I was sick, I lost my hair, I had no appetite. My taste buds changed and everything tasted metallic. I had mouth sores. I had bone pain. I had hand-foot syndrome. My eyes and nose wouldn't stop watering. My blood counts would plummet, and I ended up requiring two or three blood transfusions in addition to the chemotherapy. I was so exhausted and overwhelmed from it all. If I wasn't sleeping or puking, I was crying. I cried a lot!

I finally finished chemo (or so I thought) on May 28, 2015. One month later, on June 25, 2015, I had my bilateral mastectomy. During the surgery, they removed seventeen nodes from my right arm (five were positive for cancer) and they found two more tumors in my right breast for a total of three tumors. Tissue expanders were also placed for future reconstruction. I had to go back into surgery about a week later for a revision due to one of the incisions not wanting to heal properly and the skin dying off. Once I had completed the painful healing from the surgery, it was back to four more rounds of chemotherapy infusions. This time it was carboplatin. My oncologist said this was to mop up anything microscopic that may have been left behind. So, four rounds and I was done with chemo. Then on to radiation therapy.

Radiation started in November of 2015. I had twenty-six days total, including Thanksgiving Day. My last day of radiation was December 11, 2015, and I couldn't have been happier! My skin was literally burned from my chest through to my back and under my armpit. I was one giant, horribly blistered sunburn. But I was done!

May 12, 2016, I got my reconstruction. I was so excited! Away with those horrible expanders and hello Betty and

Veronica! It was a pretty easy recovery. I only took a week off of work and was back at it again. Taking it easy, of course, but happy to be able to get back to at least somewhat of a normal life. In August we welcomed our goofy dog Mod into the family. It was a good year.

2017 started out pretty great. Work was going well for both of us, our son was doing well in his job, we moved to a new house in a neighborhood we've always loved, and then I found it. Yes, again I found a lump. It was in the same place as the first lump in 2015. I was devastated. I was actually at a follow-up appointment with my reconstructive surgeon and asked about it. He wasn't sure what it was, so he sent me down to get an ultrasound—literally minutes later. I went back on my own while my husband waited in the waiting room. They started the ultrasound and told me it didn't look like scar tissue, but they weren't sure what it was.

I knew. In my gut I knew. I asked, "You're going to have to do a biopsy, aren't you?" They told me yes, so I asked if they could bring my husband in. They asked his name and went out to get him for me. As soon as I saw him walk in, I burst into tears. My gut was right.

On June 26, 2017, just two years and one day from the date of my bilateral mastectomy, I got the biopsy results. The cancer was back. It was a local recurrence, meaning it was in the same place and hadn't spread. Thankful for that but pissed that it was back, we knew what we had to do. We'd done this before and knew what to expect.

Chemotherapy started again in July 2017. This time was a combination of capecitabine and gemcitabine. There went my hair again and here came the side effects. Nausea, achiness, and loss of appetite, all the fun things that come with it.

My tumor showed zero response to this chemotherapy thanks to the fact I also have Stage 4 kidney disease due to a strep infection when I was a teenager.

In October 2017, I went back into surgery to have the tumor removed. Unfortunately, it was discovered the tumor had attached itself to the capsule around the implant, so my surgeon wasn't able to get the entire tumor during that surgery. I had to go back a couple of weeks later and have the remainder of the tumor, the capsule, and yes, the reconstruction removed. I went ahead and had her remove both Betty and Veronica because, well, they just had to stick together. I was upset, for sure.

Not only had I lost my real boobs, but now I've lost the replacements as well. After having the drains from the surgery removed, I ended up with a pocket of fluid that kept needing to be drained. After weeks of going in twice a week to have it drained, back into surgery I went. The surgeon removed the pocket (a seroma) and stitched my skin down so that it had nowhere to come back to.

The next step was Xeloda. What a horrible drug! My hair

grew back (extremely curly this time), but I think I had the worst case of hand-foot syndrome there ever was! My hands and feet were so swollen, red, itchy, and flaky. My palms and the bottoms of my feet literally looked and felt as if I had set them in the bottom of a searing hot frying pan. They burning feeling was unbearable at times. It hurt to walk. I would work at home just so I didn't have to hobble through the office at work because my feet were so tender to walk on. I was on the Xeloda until April of 2018 and celebrated after that last dose. I was so happy to be done with it!

Life was going back to normal again. In June 2018, I had heard about a private gym and trainer just down the street from my house who was offering a six-week fitness challenge. I joined to try to get myself back into a healthier condition.

I started out slow, working out for thirty minutes, three days a week. After a few months, I had worked my way up to thirty minutes, five days a week. My self-esteem was booming; I was losing weight and inches and feeling fantastic. In October I had a PET scan to follow-up after the Xeloda treatments. I got the call on October 18, 2018. I was N.E.D.! (No evidence of disease.) I cried from excitement. I never thought I'd hear those words. Unfortunately, they were short-lived.

In February 2019, I had another follow-up PET scan. I was expecting it to come back clear as well, but I was wrong. Very wrong. The cancer was back. It was metastatic to the left lung.

My world came crashing down. Here we go again. I'm in treatments again with no timeframe on how long it will be. My doctors have asked if I want to see a counselor or if I am a part of a support group at all. I have always avoided support groups since I have such great support from family and friends.

### Pink Sistas

That is, until I heard about Pink Sistas. I saw that they had an opening for their winter 2019 retreat. I contemplated whether or not I should try to go. I made the jump and called. I was in! I went to the retreat and am so happy I did!

I met so many amazing women who will forever be in my heart. I only wish that I had heard about Pink Sistas in 2015 when my first diagnosis came. They are amazing and a wonderful form of support! They will be the first bit of information I give to anyone I meet who is just being diagnosed.

I am still going to the gym three days a week, working full time and loving life. I try to keep everything positive and ignore any negative. This disease is a true *beast*! I have faith though that God knows what my future is and with the help of my family, friends, and now my Pink Sistas, I can do anything I put my mind to. I love you, Pink Sistas!

# Becci Owens

Becci Owens is a hardworking wife, mother, sister, friend and three-time cancer fighter.

Her passion is making the people she loves happy through her home cooking and entertaining.

Becci is an Administrative Assistant for an international snack food company where she has worked for nearly 12 years.

Becci grew up in the military, and her travels around the world during that time give her a unique perspective and insight to her fellow human beings.

Becci was born in Portland, OR, but grew up all over the world due to her father being in the Army.

She was fifteen when she met Jim, her husband of twenty-six years. They met when their fathers were stationed at Ft Lewis, Washington. Together, they have a twenty-four- year-old son, J.T., and a goofy dog named Mod.

Connect with Becci
Facebook: Becci Malone Owens
Instagram: becci jo o

"Yesterday I dared to struggle,

Today I dare to win."

~ Bernadette Devlin

# Roll of the Dice

February 2016, in the evening after getting my kids to bed, I kissed my husband good night and lay in bed to unwind and watch a reality show.

I had a scratch near my left breast in my underarm. I felt a little lump, and I thought, "That's weird." It was a pea-sized hard ball. I felt the other breast; it wasn't there. I asked my husband to feel, and he said maybe it was just from breast-feeding, but it had been months since I stopped.

I'll go to the doctor for anything. As I always tell my husband, "Safety is sexy!"

I made an appointment with my wonderful primary care

doctor, Dr. Wu. She said I was pretty young—I was thirty-five at the time—had no family history and was in good health; it was probably nothing, but she would be happy to run a mammogram for me. I agreed; I needed a mammogram just to ease my mind. It was scheduled for a week later. The machine needed repairs, so another week. I went in with my husband and the young ultrasound tech said, You can see the region right there, there's something; I'll have the radiologist look. Then I was told I needed a biopsy the next day. I was nervous going in. My husband went with me, but I thought no way did I have cancer. After all, my primary care doctor told me I was too young, and I had no family history. I thought, It's probably just benign.

The day of my biopsy, I remember chatting with the medical assistant. As we had kids around the same age, the radiologist didn't even look at me. She kept a great poker face. I remember asking how long it would take until I get the results, I was told a few days. That was the longest week ever!

I called on Friday and they said the results weren't in yet. I had to wait through the weekend. I remember my husband driving me to this park that overlooks Portland, and I said to him, "I think I have breast cancer."

He said we didn't have the results yet. I told him everything is going too well in life: my salon is taking off, you are a wonderful husband, the kids are happy . . . but I have a feeling it's cancer. We drove home and I prayed all night.

The next day, a Monday, I took my son to preschool, then came home and put my daughter in her high chair while I was making her breakfast.

The phone rang, it was the radiologist. She said, "I have your results, and I'm sorry to tell you this, but you have breast cancer."

I was shaking. She said, "Get a pen, because I need you to write down some information."

She told me it was Stage 1, estrogen positive, HER2 negative. (Whatever that means, I thought.) I was told I would need to meet with the surgeon and an oncologist.

I did not want to call my husband; he is a teacher and I didn't want to disrupt his class.

I called my mom crying, she just said, "I love you, honey; I'll talk to you later" and hung up the phone. Which is not like my mom.

Next, I called my sister. Luckily, she was on her break at work. I told her they called, and I had breast cancer.

She said, "You're going to kick this breast cancer! We're going to get you cool hats and scarves and big earrings. Don't even worry, I'm here for you." I'm more of a stressed person and my sister doesn't worry much; she's the calm to my crazy.

A few minutes later my cousin and then my brother walked through the door. My mom had called them, and they came right over. Family is everything to me, and they all are amazing!

My mom sent me a text saying she was picking my son up from preschool and coming over. The preschool teacher was one of my best friends. When she saw my mom pick up my son instead of me, she said, "Oh, Kortnee has cancer, doesn't she?" I'll always remember that the next day she gave me a box of sunshine—everything in it was yellow. It's the little things like that that I remember.

My mom told me I should call my husband, and I wish I hadn't. I said, "I'm okay, but it's cancer. Don't come home, we'll chat after work."

He said he held it together at work, then lost it on his way home. He walked through the door and we cried together and hugged. We started researching everything we could right away.

That evening my sister, my sister-in-law and my aunts all came over and brought food. I couldn't eat, I kept hyper-ventilating and crying. Trying to go to sleep that night, I kept waking up, thinking it was a nightmare. I couldn't control my tears. My husband would wake up and just hold me.

When you hear the word cancer, I thought it meant you were dying. I have a one-year-old and a three-year-old; this can't happen to me.

I had my first appointment at the amazing Compass Oncology at Providence Portland. My first oncologist was a tough personality, someone you want for oncology. I'm not sure we would ever be friends, but I wanted her as my doctor. She was great, as was the oncology surgeon, also at Providence Portland. They were both amazing.

I had to answer a lot of questions about family history, have blood tests, scans, etc. I also had to decide if I wanted a double mastectomy or a lumpectomy.

I thought of Giuliana Rancic. I used to watch her reality show. She had a double mastectomy and the show followed her journey.

Then I remembered my brother-in-law's ex-girlfriend had breast cancer when she was in her twenties. I reached out to her on Facebook. She had a lumpectomy. She said, "If I had to do it all again, I would've had a double mastectomy first," because her cancer came back. She said the only reason she chose not to was because at the time she was a single mom of two boys. She said, "Kortnee, if you have the help, get a mastectomy."

I did more research and saw more doctors for second opinions. I scheduled a double mastectomy for three weeks later. My husband told me it was my decision and he would support my choice.

I met with the plastic surgeon who would put tissue expanders in right after the double mastectomy.

The morning of my surgery, we parked at Providence Portland. There is a cross is at the top of the hospital, and a

Catholic chapel inside. I went to the chapel that morning, crying and praying was all I could do.

I had a full room of guests: my husband, my sister, my brother, sister-in-law, my mom, my dad, and my two aunts. They were all there for me.

After a long surgery, the doctors told my husband and parents they had removed the cancer and it did not spread to the lymph nodes. Hallelujah!

I remember being very sore and out of it, but seeing my family staying there all day made me feel loved.

I was in the hospital for a few days then returned home with drain tubes. My husband was the best nurse, he changed drain tubes and managed my meds. My wonderful mother-in-law "Mima" took over my mommy duties. My daughter was just one year old. She would be in her crib and I would hear her cry at night. I would walk into her room, but I couldn't pick her up. It broke my heart.

Thankfully, my mother-in-law moved in with us and would meet me in my baby girl's room and pick her up and rock her for me. I still thank her every day for all she does.

I was part of a Mom's Club and they had set up a meal train for us. Food was delivered to our home every night for thirty days; it was amazing and helped us out so much.

After recovery, I had to go in and get my tissue expanders slowly pumped up. My sister told me she thought it looked like a balloon blowing up when she took me. It stretched the muscles and was super painful. I always joked I don't know how Dolly Parton did it!

My oncologist called me and said my Oncotype score was at 11%, meaning low cancer recurring. She wanted me to start chemo in April. I had twelve rounds, once every other week for six months. I was able to have the low-dose chemo. I was happy I didn't lose my hair; however, I had a lot of side effects and definitely did not feel well.

I was able to keep working in my salon. I was also exercising. My yoga instructor was diagnosed with the same type of breast cancer as I was just one month before my diagnosis. I reached out to her, we went through our journey together, and are now great friends.

I have learned so much about health, fitness, and nutrition from her. Eating healthy and doing normal activity with my kids, husband and family. I feel blessed.

My wonderful friend Alisiha took me to my chemo appointments, and she lived almost an hour away. She kept me laughing, which really is the best medicine.

Once chemo was over, I wanted to have the expanders changed out for implants as soon as possible, because I had booked a trip to Mexico before I was diagnosed.

I really wanted saline implants because I'm more of a natural person, but my doctor talked me out of it and said the gummy bear silicone implants look best in reconstruction patients. So, I went with the doctor's recommendation.

Surgery went as expected. I was sent home with drain tubes. Unfortunately, I was chasing after my one-year-old, and I kind of tripped—and she accidently pulled the drain tube out.

I caught a breast infection and was in the hospital for five days. The Infectious Disease Control team came in every day. Luckily, they were able to drain it and the antibiotics worked. Unfortunately, I missed my Mexico vacation, but being healthy and not needing another surgery was most important.

My doctor told me I should start tamoxifen; it stops estrogen production in your body. The type of breast cancer I have is "the kind to get" because they know how to treat it: stop all estrogen.

I didn't want to take the tamoxifen because I had read all the side effects: taking it long term is not good for you. But I recalled reading Giuliana Rancic's book, and at the end of her book she noted that she looks at the pill before she takes it; she knows this pill is going to do her body good and keep her healthy, and it's worth the side effects. I think that every night as I still take tamoxifen.

Giuliana Rancic has a breast cancer foundation called Fab-U-Wish. I wrote to her foundation and told how her book and show helped me through my breast cancer journey. My wish was to meet her. I got the next best thing, a phone call from her on June 2. We were able to chat about cancer, kids, life, and health. Best. Gift. Ever. I admire her and look up to her so much!

My oncologists suggested that since I'd had two children, I should likely get a hysterectomy. I was doing monthly shots in my tummy to put me in menopause to stop my estrogen. I had three doctors' opinions, and they all recommended it since my cancer was estrogen-positive.

November 2017, I had the hysterectomy. The surgery went as expected, and recovery was not as bad as the other surgeries. It was difficult in my mid-thirties to be in my first year of going into menopause; I didn't feel normal, it was so hard physically and emotionally. This is another chapter to write on, next time!

## Pink Sistas

My retreat weekend will always hold a special place in my heart. Deb is so welcoming; from the moment you walk in the door. She made me feel so comfortable and the retreat weekend took my mind off of my life issues and allowed me to relax.

There was paddle boarding, yoga, amazing food, and conversation with the other women on the retreat.

I tell so many people about Pink Sistas retreats. It was nice to share my story and listen to the stories of other women who are going through it all, too.

Whenever I have fear or anxiety (which is often) I still think of the conversations I have had with Deb. Not only during my retreat weekend, but also in phone calls and messages.

If I could give a humanitarian award, it would be awarded to Deb Hart for all she has done – not only for me, but for other breast cancer survivors and thrivers.

## Toxic Implants

In 2019, I began feeling ill, right before the Pink Sistas retreat. I thought it may have been due to the side effects of chemo, tamoxifen, or menopause.

I had a checkup with my plastic surgeon and found out the silicone implants were on a recall. Some were leaking and causing cancer of the immune system. Luckily mine were not leaking, but I was having weird symptoms. I was seeing my naturopathic doctor and medical doctor, and every test was coming back normal. But I was lightheaded, I had vision issues, nerve issues, and I was so weak and tired.

I decided I wanted these toxic implants taken out. I had the implants removed in November 2019 and replaced them with saline implants. Dr. Bartholomew did a wonderful job swapping implants. The saline implants look and feel more comfortable and natural than the silicone ones had. I'm feeling better now in February 2020.

I have learned so much about health, hormones, cancer,

supplements vitamins, exercise, and food. It has been life-changing for me. I still ask every Eastern and Western doctor I see, "Why do you think I got breast cancer?"

I was told one in eight women get breast cancer. Line up eight friends, roll the dice, and one of you will get it. Your age and family history doesn't matter, one in eight will get it.

I'm doing everything I can to keep myself healthy and stress free. I would like to share everything I know now and what I've been through, so please feel free to contact me.

## Thank You

Thank you to Compass Oncology; A Woman's Time—Dr. Tori Hudson, Dr. Rebecca Reese, Dr. Wu, Dr. Imatani, Dr. Bartholomew, Dr. Finch, Dr. Krien, and Dr. Drake.

Deb Hart and Pink Sistas, and Dr. Solti, the sweetest oncologist. My physical therapists. All my family and friends. My mother-in-law, Mima.

My son and daughter, who always remind me to slow down and Namaste. They ask, "Is this healthy to eat?" And they wake me up to start yoga every morning.

My biggest cheerleading doctor, nurse, teacher, researcher, comedian, and loving husband . . . *I love you!*

Peace, love, health, and happiness to you all!

# Kortnee Colbry

Kortnee Colbry is a esthetician and the owner of Eyeland Beauty.

She graduated from Boise State University and is a devoted Bronco fan.

Kortnee has an amazing husband and two awesome kids, a seven-year-old son and five-year-old daughter.

She loves Yoga and the Hawaiian Islands.

She is passionate about researching health and nutrition.

Connect with Kortnee
Instagram: @eyelandbeautykortnee
Website: www.eyelandbeauty.com

Keep putting one foot in front of the other.

That's all you need to do right now.

# Strength and Perseverance

In 2012, I had my first child and I weighed almost 300 pounds. I had been obese for most of my life. Diets? I'd tried them all, and failed. Or, at least if I'd managed to lose any significant amount of weight on them, I'd gain it all back, and then some once I quit.

A few weeks after my son was born, a friend, who'd had great success recently in losing weight asked me to join Weight Watchers with her. I begrudgingly agreed, and spent the first six months just treading water, not making much progress.

One day, I resolved that I was going to finally stick with it.

I honestly don't know what clicked, but it did. It took me three years, but I managed to lose over 140 pounds. I had taken up running, and completed several 5k's, 8k's and 10k's. In 2015, I was invited to be on a Hood to Coast team for the first time in my life.

If you've never heard of Hood to Coast (or HTC), it's a 199-mile relay run from the top of Mt. Hood to Seaside, Oregon. It spans about thirty-five hours, with teams of twelve, and each team member runs three legs totaling around fifteen miles per person. It's such a magical and empowering experience, after my first relay, I was hooked.

The Hood to Coast is a highly coveted event. Teams come from all over the world to compete—and the team selection is done by lottery, so it's not a guarantee that your team will get in. In 2018, I decided that I wanted to create a fundraising team, which guaranteed our entry, as long as we raised at least ten thousand dollars. The beneficiary of the Hood to Coast is Providence Cancer Institute.

Our team ended up surpassing our goal and raised almost twenty thousand dollars in the first year. We signed up to fundraise again for the 2019 relay almost as soon as we finished that first year. We were on a roll and wanted to keep going.

I first found my lump in June of 2018. I was in the shower one day and noticed it by accident. Because of my major weight loss, I had a lot of very thin and sagging skin, and my hand ran over something that felt odd. I was breastfeeding my second child, at that time, and assumed it was a clogged milk duct. When it didn't go away, I made an appointment to see my primary care physician. She agreed that it felt like a clogged duct but sent me in for an ultrasound to have it looked at anyway. The ultrasound results were consistent with cystic matter, and the radiologist suggested I come back for a follow-up ultrasound in six months.

In the meantime, I ran my first half marathon and then had a breast lift and tummy tuck, to remove all of that extra skin from my weight loss. I returned to running again within just a few weeks, and I was feeling great.

I probably would have forgotten to follow up with that ultrasound, but right on time, I received an email reminding me to schedule my appointment. I wasn't sure if I needed to schedule though the hospital directly, or through my physician's office, so it took a while to get the appointment.

Something nagged at me, making me strive to ensure I went in for that follow-up. I had mentioned to a friend that sometimes when I ran, my upper left breast was sore. After days of trying, on my thirty-sixth birthday, I got through finally and booked the appointment. Honestly, the day I went in for that follow-up, I thought it would be routine, and I'd be in and out of there in a few minutes.

My world was turned upside down that day, Tuesday, February 19, 2019. At first, it felt like a routine exam. I've had my fair share of ultrasounds. It's normal to hear the buttons click as they are taking pictures of what they are looking at.

Eventually the technician asked me to take my arm out of the sleeve on my gown, so he could look in my armpit, and then the clicks started. I was silently thinking, "What is in my armpit that he is looking at?"

He finished and said he was going to get the radiologist to have her look at the pictures. He also asked if I had any history of breast cancer in my family, which caught me off guard.

Before I knew it, I had had my very first mammogram, and was back in the ultrasound room for a more in-depth look at my right breast. There were three places of interest to the radiologist, and she scheduled me for a biopsy the next morning.

I'm not sure how I held it together as I walked out of the hospital, but as soon as I got in the car, I called my mom and burst into tears. "I can't have cancer; I have two little kids!" was all I kept saying. She insisted that she would be attending the biopsy with me.

After the doctor performed the biopsy the next day, she told me what she thought—that it was cancer. She listed a few different types that it looked like and said it would be confirmed with the pathology report, which could take five to seven days. Once she left the room, the tears started again, and I cried, "I can't have cancer, I fundraise for cancer research! This isn't fair!"

I spent the next day in one of my favorite places, skiing with my stepmom, who had her own battle with breast cancer in 2002. She went through the gamut of chemo and had a mastectomy. She shared with me all of the things she had gone through.

Today, I feel bad that I wasn't more involved when she was in treatment; I was just nineteen, and I didn't understand the magnitude of the situation. That entire day, I had a feeling the results would come back as cancer. As soon as we got home that afternoon, I received a call confirming that I had Invasive Ductal Carcinoma, a common form of breast cancer.

The rest of the day is a blur, but I clearly remember when my general physician called me; all she had to do was say my name, and I broke down. She's been my doctor since I was twelve years old, and it was like talking to my mom. She assured me that we would be fighting this. She gave me the names of some great oncology doctors that she wanted me to see right away.

The next two weeks were incredibly busy. At my first appointment, my medical oncologist told me I would have to have six rounds of TCHP chemotherapy, administered every three weeks, and then either a lumpectomy or a mastectomy (my choice) after that.

The first thing I did was go through my calendar to make

sure I'd be done in time to run Hood to Coast, and I told him that. He laughed at me. He probably thought I was insane—here he was telling me I had Stage 2, triple-positive breast cancer, and I was telling him about how my event at the end of August was going to need to be worked in.

During that two weeks, I had a port catheter placed, so that chemotherapy could be administered, a PET scan to see if the cancer had spread to anywhere else in my body, a breast MRI, and an echocardiogram to get a baseline on my heart, since chemo can cause heart failure.

On the day of my first chemo, just thirteen days after that follow-up ultrasound, I got up early and ran five miles before I took my son to school and headed to the doctor.

I was so lucky that my dad and stepmom insisted on taking my kids for the weekends when I was going through chemo. Having them at home would have been rough. I had my infusions on Wednesday, and by Friday, I was out of it, sleeping twenty hours of the day. Saturday and Sunday were miserable. Because I couldn't sleep or focus on reading or watching movies, the minutes took forever to pass. By Monday morning, I would force myself to get up and walk my son to school again.

I usually would give myself about a week to recover before I would start running again, and I averaged about thirty miles between treatments. One week after my last treatment, I hosted our annual fundraising garage sale at my house. It was a lot of work, and I was exhausted, but it was for a great cause!

I also continued to get up and run on the morning of every infusion. My nurses, when I would get there, started to ask, "How many miles did you run this morning?"

As scheduled, I had my lumpectomy with axillary lymph node dissection on July 18. The hope was that the chemo would have destroyed all of the cancer, but it wasn't completely wiped out. I had a little remaining in my breast, and one of the nineteen lymph nodes that were removed was positive. Not all bad, though, the surgeon was able to get all of it out and produce clear margins.

Here's where it gets cool—a new treatment was released in May of 2019 for patients with HER2+, lower stage breast cancer, with residual cancer after chemo, called Kadcyla. A mixture of mild chemotherapy and hormone suppression agent, it targets the HER2 cells and reduces the recurrence rate significantly.

Previously it was used only in Stage 4 breast and lung cancer patients to prevent spread and prolong life. Remember the fundraising for cancer research I mentioned earlier? I am a direct beneficiary of cancer research!

So, while I do have to have fourteen rounds of this Kadcyla stuff—an infusion every three weeks—I'm so excited to know that my chances of having my cancer come back are so much lower.

## Pink Sistas

Around the time of my surgery, I was contacted by Deb Hart. She had met with my uncle Brad, looking for a donation of a motor for her pontoon boat.

After she finished telling him all about what Pink Sistas does, he told her that his niece was currently battling breast cancer and asked if she would be able to squeeze me in on a retreat weekend.

She had barely left his shop before she was on the phone, telling me all about her retreats. Not only did she find a space for me, she also found room for my friend Angela, whom I had met through this cancer process.

The retreat was the weekend before Hood to Coast, at a big decision point in my journey. I literally had just come from a radiation consultation.

Through the entire process, I had always thought I would be able to skip radiation by having a mastectomy instead, but due to the residual cancer at surgery, it was highly recommended I do thirty rounds of radiation. I'd also been given some conflicting information, so I was extremely confused.

I had a wonderful time on Deb's gorgeous floating home. She takes hospitality to a whole new level by giving up all of her personal space to ten women every weekend. She is up at 5:00 am, starting the day with coffee, entertaining the entire time, and never lets a guest lift a finger. I was able to make some friendships with a variety of other survivors, along with trying yoga on the dock for the first time.

We took sunset cruises on the pontoon boat, laughed and cried together, made jewelry to keep as a reminder of our weekend together, and all for free.

My wish is that every survivor is able to attend one of her retreats in their lifetime!

After my retreat weekend, I ran my fourth Hood to Coast! Our team finished our second fundraising year with over $18,000!

## Strength and Perseverance

During my daytime runs, I wore shirts that said, "I'm kicking cancer's butt! What's your superpower?" and "Cancer picked the wrong bitch!" on the back.

I had numerous people give me words of encouragement as they passed me on each of my legs, and it meant so much.

It's funny, the first year as a fundraising team, we thought we were raising money for a great cause. This year had a whole new meaning. Not only had I been diagnosed with breast cancer, but a thirty-four-year-old teammate was diagnosed with testicular cancer in January, his father with prostate cancer.

I was the leg twelve runner, which meant I was the last runner on our team and got to finish along the boardwalk in Seaside with crowds cheering me on, and then ran onto the sand to meet the rest of my team to cross the finish line together. Finishing that run meant more to me than any prior year, I was determined to meet a goal, and I had achieved it.

I did go through thirty rounds of radiation and decided not to have the mastectomy. The recurrence rate if I'd had the surgery was only 1% better than it is with the other things we're doing. The radiation for me really wasn't terrible.

I still have some pain in my left breast when I run, and I'm going to physical therapy for some aftereffects in my arm from the surgery. I'm told it will get better, but it could take time, possibly years.

I completed my second half marathon (Girlfriends Run for A Cure in Vancouver, Washington) during radiation, and then my third half marathon in Las Vegas shortly after radiation was over. In 2019, I logged more miles than any prior year (over 900)—even when I was in the best shape of my life! If I hadn't been diagnosed, I wouldn't have had a reason to push myself this year. If my doctor hadn't laughed and told me I wouldn't likely be running HTC, I wouldn't have tried so hard to show him I would.

My battle isn't over, I still have to finish up my Kadcyla infusions, and will be on oral hormone suppression therapy for the next ten years. I may even end up having my ovaries removed at some point.

I think it happened to me so I can bring awareness, and positivity to a devastating diagnosis. I saw my life flash before my eyes, and now I don't take any experiences for granted. I cherish more moments with my kids, husband, friends, and family. I look into the horizon and admire my surroundings. I take opportunities to try new things. It's important for me to show strength and perseverance in everything I do.

# Shannon Preston

Shannon Preston lives in Oregon City, Oregon with her husband, their son Lucas, daughter Avery and their one hundred pound Labrador, Dexter.

She worked in the escrow industry for many years before making the decision to stay home with her children.

Currently, Shannon is the bookkeeper for her husband's small business, along with the captain of her fundraising team.

Her hobbies include running, snow skiing, camping and watching football with her family. She also enjoys searching for a fantastic Bloody Mary with friends.

Connect with Shannon:
Facebook: @Shannon Preston

# ACKNOWLEDGEMENTS

To each woman who has joined us on a Pink Sistas retreat, we are so grateful to have been part of your journey.

To our friends and families, thank you is not enough. Please accept our deepest gratitude for everything you do for us, we could not continue with the mission of Pink Sistas without you.

To our volunteers and the board members of Pink Sistas, you are truly angels on earth. Thank you for your time and commitment to our organization. You make a difference each day.

To our supporters, thank you for your donations. As a non-profit organization we depend on you, and you continually surprise and amaze us with your generousity.

To our corporate sponsors, you are the backbone of our organization, without your support we would not be able to offer Pink Sistas retreats at no cost to the women we serve.

WESTON

BUICK KIA GMC

We would like to sincerely thank Weston Kia, our very first corporate sponsor. Weston Kia and Pink Sistas have been in partnership for nine years. We are incredibly grateful for their support and generosity. Jan Weston has become a great friend and a wise mentor.

Jan Weston and the Weston Kia family donated our party barge, the TICKLED PINK. Weston Kia sponsors our annual fundraising event, Pink in the Gorge and the Pink Sistas calendar. Thank you, Jan Weston and Weston Kia!

Fred Meyer has been a valued corporate partner of Pink Sistas for eight years. They are a presenting sponsor for our Pink in the Gorge annual fundraiser, and they provide all of our printing needs, including the Pink Sistas calendars. They also generously donate swag bags for our retreat guests.

Each year, Fred Meyer sponsors a Pink Sistas weekend retreat for employees of Fred Meyer who have been diagnosed with breast cancer. Thank you, Fred Meyer!

# HOW YOU CAN HELP

Pink Sistas is dedicated to honor, support, and help women affected by a diagnosis of breast cancer. We would not be able to serve our community of women without your generous donations and continued support.

Your donations allow us to continue our mission by providing important resources, new venues for our retreats, and increase breast cancer awareness in our community.

To donate, sponsor, or volunteer, please visit https://pinksistas.org/howyoucanhelp/

# Glossary

**AlloDerm**

ADM stands for "acellular dermal matrix." It is a biologic mesh-like material derived from animals or donated (cadaveric) human skin. AlloDerm and other similar ADM products are used routinely in breast reconstruction.

**Biopsy**

Removal of tissue to be tested for cancer cells.

**BRCA1 and BRCA2 (BRCA1/2) Gene Mutations**

Genes that help limit cell growth.

A mutation (change) in one of these genes increases a person's risk of breast, ovarian, and certain other cancers. Everyone has BRCA1 and BRCA2 genes.

**DIEP Flap Reconstruction**

A deep inferior epigastric artery perforator (DIEP) flap is a type of breast reconstruction procedure. During DIEP flap reconstruction surgery, a surgeon will take healthy tissue, skin, and fat from the person's lower abdomen to use in breast reconstruction.

**Early Breast Cancer**

Cancer that is contained in the breast or has only spread to lymph nodes in the underarm area. This term often describes Stage 1 and Stage 2 breast cancer.

**Hand-Foot Syndrome**

Hand-foot syndrome is also called palmar plantar erythrodysesthesia. It is a side effect of some cancer treatments. Hand-foot syndrome causes redness, swelling, and pain on the palms of the hands and/or the soles of the feet.

**HER2-Positive (HER2+) Breast Cancer**

In about 20% of breast cancers, the cells make too much of a protein known as HER2 (Human Epidermal Growth Factor Receptor 2, HER2/neu, erbB2). These cancers tend to be aggressive and fast-growing.

HER2-negative (HER–) breast cancers have little or no HER2 protein. HER2-positive (HER+) breast cancers have a lot of HER2 protein. HER2+ tumors can be treated with HER2-targeted therapies, such as trastuzumab (Herceptin).

**Inflammatory Breast Cancer (IBC)**

A rare, aggressive form of invasive breast cancer whose main symptoms are swelling (inflammation) and redness of the breast. The skin on the breast may look dimpled, like the skin of an orange, and may be warm to the touch.

**Invasive Breast Cancer**

Cancer that has spread from the original location (milk ducts or lobules) into the surrounding breast tissue and possibly into the lymph nodes and other parts of the body. Invasive ductal cancer begins in the milk ducts. Invasive lobular cancer begins in the lobules of the breast.

**Invasive Ductal Carcinoma**

IDC, also known as infiltrating ductal carcinoma, is cancer that began growing in a milk duct and has invaded the fibrous or fatty tissue of the breast outside of the duct. IDC is the most common form of breast cancer, representing eighty percent of all breast cancer diagnoses.

**Lumpectomy (Breast Conserving Surgery)**

Breast surgery that removes only the tumor and a small rim of normal tissue around it, leaving most of the breast skin and tissue in place.

**Margins**

The rim of normal tissue surrounding a tumor that's removed during breast surgery.

A margin is clean (also known as uninvolved, negative or clear) if there's only normal tissue (and no cancer cells) at the edges. Clean margins show the entire tumor was removed.

With involved (positive) margins, normal tissue doesn't completely surround the tumor. This means the entire tumor was not removed and more surgery may be needed to get clean margins.

**Mastectomy**

Surgical removal of the breast. The exact procedure depends on the diagnosis.

**Metastatic Breast Cancer**

Breast cancer that has spread beyond the breast to other organs in the body (most often the bones, lungs, liver or brain). Metastatic breast cancer is not a specific type of breast cancer, but rather the most advanced stage (Stage 4) of breast cancer.

**N.E.D.**

No evidence of disease (NED) is often used with cancer when there is no physical evidence of the disease on examination or imaging tests after treatment. No evidence of disease means the same thing as complete remission or complete response. It does not, however, mean that a cancer is cured.

**Onoctype score**

The Oncotype DX test is a genomic test that analyzes the activity of a group of twenty-one genes from a breast cancer tissue sample that can affect how a cancer is likely to behave and respond to treatment.

**Papanicolaou (Pa′-puh-Nih′-koh-low)**

A procedure in which a small brush or spatula is used to gently remove cells from the cervix so they can be checked under a microscope for cervical cancer or cell changes that may lead to cervical cancer.

**PET Scan**

A Positron Emission Tomography (PET) scan is an

imaging test that helps reveal how your tissues and organs are functioning. A PET scan uses a radioactive drug (tracer) to show this activity.

A PET scan is useful in revealing or evaluating several conditions, including many cancers, heart disease and brain disorders. Often, PET images are combined with CT or MRI scans to create special views.

**Prophylactic Mastectomy**

Surgery to remove one or both breasts to reduce the risk of developing breast cancer.

According to the National Cancer Institute, prophylactic mastectomy in women who carry a BRCA1 or BRCA2 gene mutation may be able to reduce the risk of developing breast cancer by 95%.

**Scalp Cooling**

The use of a cap filled with a chilled substance during chemotherapy to reduce hair loss due to chemotherapy.

**Seroma**

A seroma is a collection of fluid that builds up under the surface of your skin. Seromas may develop after a surgical procedure, most often at the site of the surgical incision or where tissue was removed.

**Tamoxifen (Nolvadex)**

A hormone therapy drug (taken in pill form) used to treat

early and advanced stage breast cancers that are hormone receptor-positive. These breast cancers need estrogen to grow. Tamoxifen stops or slows the growth of these tumors by blocking estrogen from attaching to hormone receptors in the cancer cells.

**Triple Negative Breast Cancer**

A breast cancer that is estrogen receptor-negative, progesterone receptor-negative and HER2-negative.

# Julie Pershing

*Waves of Pink: Stories of Sisterhood* started as an idea to bring attention to the important work Pink Sistas does for the breast cancer community.

I approached my good friend Deb Hart and asked if she thought the women who went to the Pink Sistas retreats would be willing to tell their stories.

The tangible result of that first conversation (and many more to follow), is the book you have in your hand. A powerful collection of real-life stories.

It's not easy to write your story, especially when you are writing about something as personal and life-changing as a cancer diagnosis. I am so grateful the women in this book said yes.

Your story matters. If you are ready to write a book, I would love to be a part of your journey.

Connect with Julie:
Email: hello@gallivantpress.com
Website: https://gallivantpress.com/

Free 30 minute consultation:
https://gallivantpress.as.me/consult

GALLIVANT
PRESS

Made in the USA
Middletown, DE
23 April 2021